Practical Plant Physiology

Practical Plant Physiology

J. Roberts, BSc, AKC, MIBiol
D. G. Whitehouse, PhD, BSc, DIC

Longman
London and New York

Longman Group Limited London

Associated companies, branches and representatives throughout the world

Published in the United States of America by Longman Inc., New York

© Longman Group Limited 1976

First published 1976
Reprinted 1978

Library of Congress Cataloging in Publication Data

Roberts, J.
    Practical plant physiology.

    Includes index.
    1. Plant physiology — Laboratory manuals.
I. Whitehouse, D. G., joint author. II. Title.
QK714.5.R6 581.1'028 75—46566
ISBN 0 582 44127 7

Set in IBM Journal 10 on 12pt
and printed in Great Britain by
Lowe and Brydone (Printers) Ltd,
Thetford, Norfolk

Preface

It is intended that this text should offer a selection of tests and experiments in plant physiology and biochemistry suitable for use (with possible simplification or sophistication) at GCE Advanced Level (or its equivalent) and certain introductory undergraduate courses.

The units and nomenclature used in the text conform in the main to the SI system. It is realised that many laboratories will have glassware and equipment calibrated in non-SI units and that many of those performing the experiments will be more familiar with previously used units of measurement. Conversion tables may be found in Appendix 5 and in the text certain 'pre-SI units' are bracketed to assist change to the SI system.

Where appropriate materials suggested are considered to be adequate for a class of 10 students. For some experiments the question of whether students perform the experiments individually or in groups will depend upon the availability of equipment and accommodation; for these experiments the specification of quantities would have little value. However, in all cases we have tried to show an awareness of the low budget on which many laboratories operate; some experiments have been modified with this in mind. For many experiments variations utilising the techniques and principles are feasible and the authors consider it desirable that students are encouraged to consider such variations and participate in designing such experiments. To this end suggested experiments and project work will be found at the end of each chapter.

We have accumulated this knowledge of practical work over several years and in some cases the original source of the experiments is no longer known. Some of the experiments have, however, originated from known sources and we wish to thank gratefully Professor D. A. Walker of the University of Sheffield and Professor P. F. Wareing of the University College of Wales, Aberystwyth, whose kind permission has been granted for the use of experiments which originated from their laboratories. In the final analysis however any mistakes remain our responsibility.

J. Roberts and D. G. Whitehouse
Department of Applied Biology
N.E. London Polytechnic
London E15 4LZ

Contents

1 Carbohydrates

Introduction

Carbohydrates are compounds made up of carbon, hydrogen and oxygen; certain members of the group also contain nitrogen and sulphur. Originally, as the name implies, carbohydrates were thought to be hydrates of carbon and could be represented as $C_x (H_2O)_y$, with a ratio of hydrogen to oxygen of $2:1$. It is now known that there are compounds which have the properties of carbohydrates but do not fulfil this simple ratio. One such example is deoxyribose, whose formula is $C_5H_{10}O_4$. Deoxyribose is a constituent of DNA. The carbohydrates may be better defined as polyhydroxy aldehydes or ketones, or as substances that yield one of these compounds on hydrolysis. They are of special importance as they compose more than 50% of the dry weight of a plant.

Carbohydrates can be classified into three groups: monosaccharides, oligosaccharides and polysaccharides. Monosaccharides are sugars that cannot be hydrolysed (under mild conditions) into simpler units. Monosaccharides are themselves classified by the number of carbon atoms they contain. Thus trioses have three carbon atoms, tetroses have four, pentoses have five, hexoses have six and so on up to the nonoses with nine carbon atoms.

The oligosaccharides are sugars composed of two or more monosaccharide units linked together by a glycosidic bond. These sugars are further distinguished as disaccharides (yielding two monosaccharide units on hydrolysis), trisaccharides and so on.

The third group, the polysaccharides, are molecules composed of large numbers of monosaccharide units linked by glycosidic bonds. There is no sharp distinction between the higher numbered oligosaccharides and the polysaccharides.

1.1 Monosaccharides

A large number of monosaccharides occur in plant tissues and of these perhaps the best known are glucose and fructose.

Glucose can exist in chain and ring forms. There is ample evidence that the ring forms of glucose predominate over the chain structure with which they are in equilibrium. Ring structures are formed because the hydroxyl group on carbon atom 4 or 5 of the glucose molecule can react with the aldehyde group on carbon atom 1 of the same molecule to give a heterocyclic five- or six-membered ring. The six-membered ring is illustrated below:

a-D-glucose D-glucose *β*-D-glucose

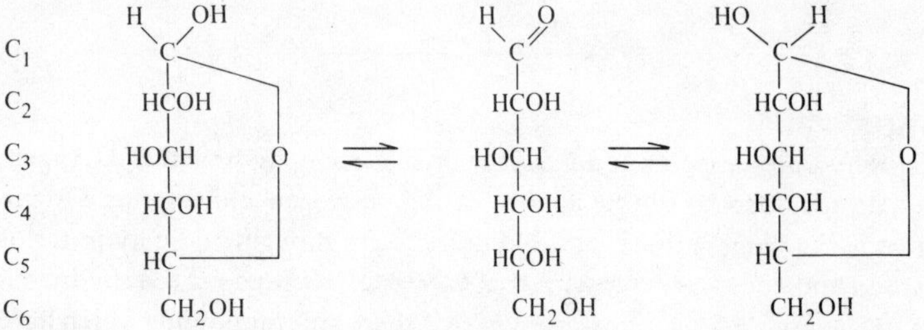

The five-membered ring is known as a 'furanose' ring and the six-membered ring as a 'pyranose' ring, because of their relationship to the heterocyclic compounds furan and pyran. The pyranose forms of the sugar predominate in nature:

Furanose structure

Furan

Pyranose structure

Pyran

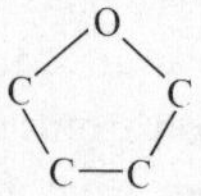

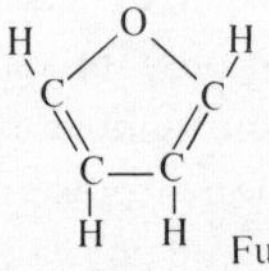

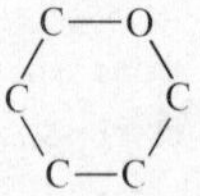

The cyclic forms of the carbohydrates are usually represented by structural formulae. Here the pyranose ring is drawn as a hexagon that lies in a plane at right angles to the page. The thickened lines indicate the atoms of the hexagon that are nearer to the viewer:

a-D-glucose

β-D-glucose

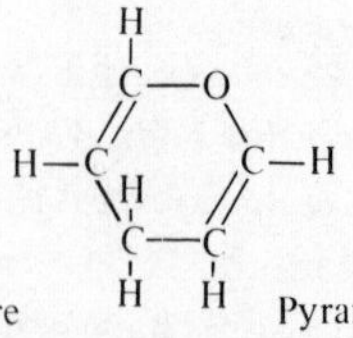

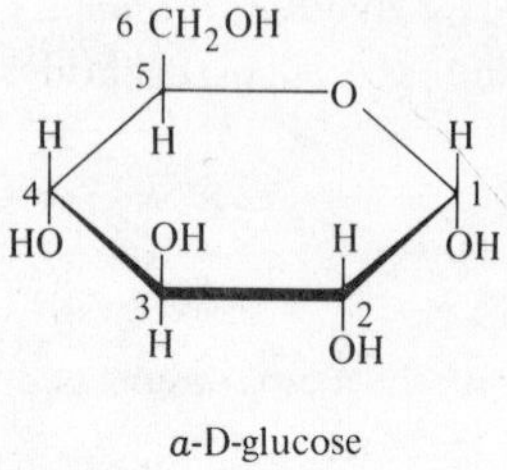

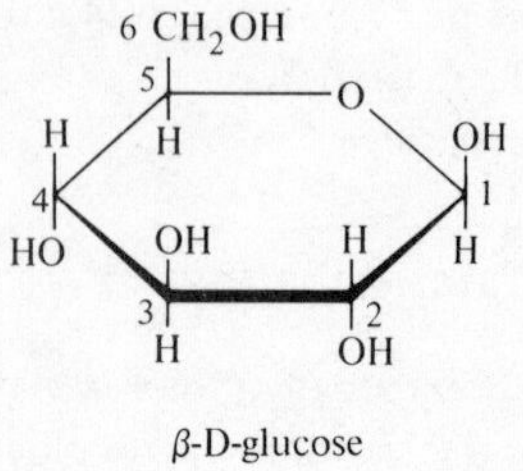

By convention the thickening of the lines, the carbon atoms in the ring and the hydrogen atoms are omitted. Only the position of the hydroxyl groups is indicated; these lie either above or below the plane of the ring. A similar situation is seen with fructose. The open chain form is in equilibrium with the corresponding pyranose and furanose forms. The furanose ring is illustrated; here the carbonyl group on the carbon atom 2 reacts with the hydroxyl group on carbon atom 5 of the same molecule:

α-D-fructose   D-fructose   β-D-fructose

Monosaccharides, such as glucose, which contain an aldehyde group are known as aldoses whilst those which contain a keto group, such as fructose, are ketoses. Sugars may be designated as α- or β-forms according to the position of the hydroxyl group on carbon 1 in the aldoses and carbon 2 in the ketoses. When this group lies on the same side of the planar ring as carbon 6 the sugar is said to be β whilst when it lies on the opposite side, it is called α:

α-D-glucose   β-D-glucose

As the ring forms are in equilibrium with their open chain forms, reagents can react with the aldehyde or keto groups of the sugars and so remove the open chain forms from the equilibrium. Thus the aldoses and ketoses can be oxidised by metallic ions which in turn are reduced (a fuller description of oxidation—reduction processes is given in Chapter 5 — Respiration). Use of this property is made in both the qualitative and quantitative assay of sugars. Those sugars with a free, or potentially free, aldehyde or keto group are thus known as reducing sugars.

Another property of monosaccharides is their reaction with strong mineral acids to form furfural derivatives:

Pentose $\xrightarrow[\text{heat}]{\text{Acid}}$ CHO   Furfural

Hexose $\xrightarrow[\text{heat}]{\text{Acid}}$ HOCH$_2$ CHO   Hydroxymethyl furfural

The furfurals will react with a variety of compounds to form coloured products. This dehydration reaction is the basis of the Molisch test (exp. 1) and other qualitative tests for carbohydrates (exps. 4, 5 and 6).

A very useful method for distinguishing between the monosaccharides is the reaction of sugars with phenylhydrazine to form crystalline osazones:

$$
\begin{array}{l}
\text{CHO} \\
\text{HCOH} \\
\text{HOCH} \\
\text{HCOH} \\
\text{HCOH} \\
\text{CH}_2\text{OH}
\end{array}
+ 3C_6H_5NHNH_2 \longrightarrow
\begin{array}{l}
\text{CH} = \text{NNHC}_6H_5 \\
\text{C} = \text{NNHC}_6H_5 \\
\text{HOCH} \\
\text{HCOH} \\
\text{HCOH} \\
\text{CH}_2\text{OH}
\end{array}
+ C_6H_5NH_2 + NH_3 + 2H_2O
$$

Glucose   Phenylhydrazine   Glucosazone

Osazones have characteristic crystal forms and colours (exp. 7).

1.2 Oligosaccharides

Disaccharides are the commonest oligosaccharides found in plant material. Sucrose is the most important of these and consists of a molecule of glucose linked to one of fructose. Sucrose will not reduce metallic ions and thus is a non-reducing sugar. Hence the reducing groups in both molecules must be involved in the glycosidic bond between the two monosaccharide units. Since the aldehyde group is on carbon atom 1 of glucose and the keto group is on carbon atom 2 of fructose the glycosidic bond is formed between these carbon atoms.

The glucose is in the pyranose form whilst the fructose is in the furanose form:

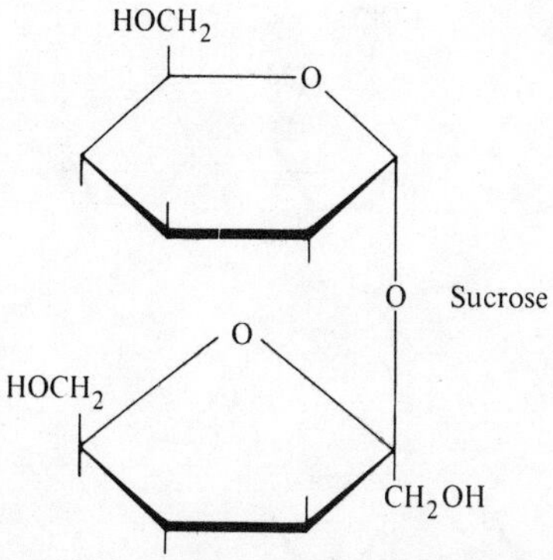

HOCH$_2$

O   Sucrose

HOCH$_2$

O

CH$_2$OH

Maltose is another disaccharide found in plants, although only in trace amounts. In this sugar one molecule of glucose is linked to a second molecule of glucose. Maltose is a reducing sugar and so there is a potentially free aldehyde group. The linkage between the two glucose units is between carbon atoms 1 and 4:

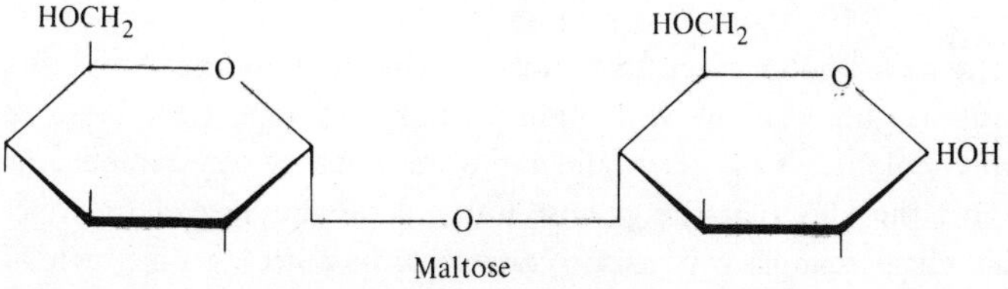

HOCH$_2$ HOCH$_2$

O   O

HOH

O

Maltose

1.3 Polysaccharides

The polysaccharides found in plant tissues may serve structural or metabolic functions. The metabolic polysaccharides of importance are starch and inulin. Starch consists of two components, amylose and amylopectin. Amylose is a linear polysaccharide composed of a large number (300 or more) glucose units linked together through carbon atoms 1 and 4. It is important to note that the amyloses vary in size from plant to plant but nevertheless have the same linear structure.

The amylopectins are branched molecules. Here short linear chains (α-1,4-linked glucose units) are joined together by 1,6-linkages. Most starches contain 20% amylose though waxy corn starch is 100% amylo-pectin:

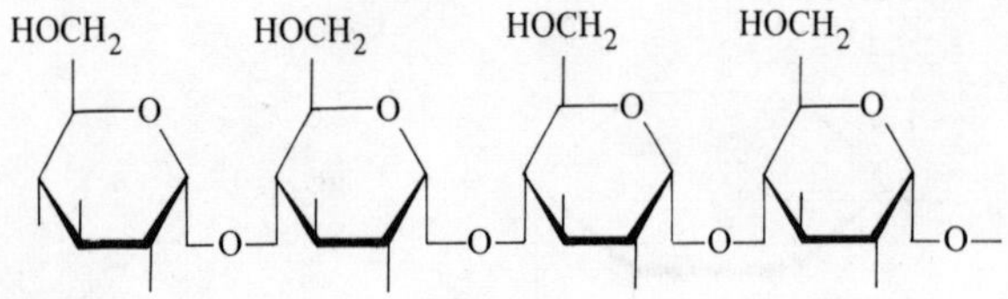

Amylose

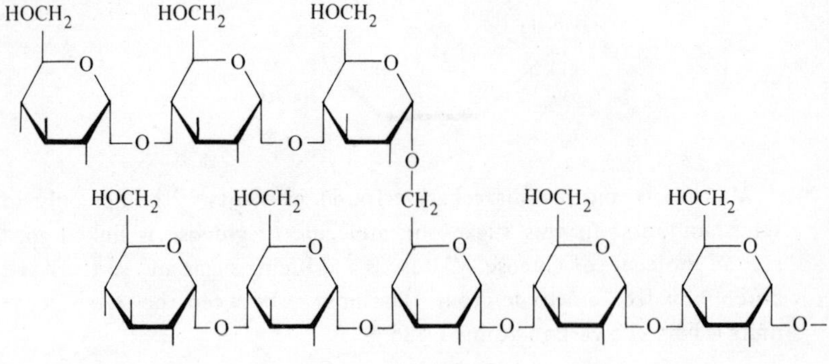

Amylopectin

The best known reaction of starch is that with iodine. Amylose gives an intense blue colour with iodine whilst amylopectin gives a red to purple colour. X-ray crystallographic studies of crystalline amylose support the idea that the glucose units in the amylose chain are coiled in a helical manner with six pyranose units forming one turn of the helix. The inner dimensions of the helix are such that an iodine molecule can be accommodated inside it. The deep blue colour is thought to be due to this amylose—iodine complex. With amylopectin the branching points interfere with the formation of the complex and it is less intensely coloured. Likewise short-chain polysaccharides (dextrins) of eight or more glucose units will give red complexes with iodine.

Inulin occurs as a reserve polysaccharide in certain members of the *Compositae* and *Campanulaceae*. Analysis indicates that inulin consists of about 33 fructofuranose units (i.e. fructose in the furanose form) joined by β-2,1-glycosidic bonds with glucose as the terminal unit at the non-reducing end. It does not stain with iodine.

The best known structural polysaccharide is cellulose which is made up of a linear chain of glucopyranose units linked by β-1,4-glycosidic bonds. Hydrolysis with mineral acids leads to the production of β-glucopyranose:

Cellulose

Experiments 1–9

The following experiments may be performed either with tissue extracts or more conveniently using standard sugar solutions. With each test an attempt should be made to assess the limits of sensitivity by diluting sugar solutions until no recognisable reaction can be found.

1: Molisch test for all carbohydrates

Materials: 200 cm^3 each of 1% solutions of fructose, glucose, maltose starch, sucrose and xylose. Store at 0°–5°C
25 cm^3 of alcoholic α-naphthol — dissolve 0.25 g of α-naphthol in 25 cm^3 of 95% ethanol
50 cm^3 concentrated sulphuric acid
70 test tubes
10 each of 1 cm^3 and 5 cm^3 pipettes

Method: Pipette 2–3 cm^3 of each of the sugar solutions into separate test tubes. To each tube add 0.5 cm^3 of α-naphthol and mix the contents. Incline each tube and slowly run 1 cm^3 of concentrated sulphuric acid down the side of the tube. A positive result is given by the formation of a purple colour at the junction of the liquids. Repeat using water instead of carbohydrate solution.

Discussion: This test is a qualitative one for all carbohydrates. The concentrated acid hydrolyses any glycosidic bonds present in the solution. This is followed by furfural (or furfural derivative) formation. These react further with α-naphthol to form a purple product.

2: Fehling's test for reducing sugars

Materials: Sugar solutions from exp. 1

Solution A — dissolve 3.5 g of copper sulphate in 50 cm^3 water

Solution B — dissolve 17.5 g sodium potassium tartrate and 5 g sodium hydroxide in 50 cm^3 water

Sulphuric acid from exp. 1

Solid sodium carbonate

100 boiling tubes

Boiling-water bath

Stop-clock

50 of 2 cm^3 pipettes

Method: Mix equal volumes of solutions A and B to give Fehling's solution. Pipette 2 cm^3 of the 1% carbohydrate solutions into separate boiling tubes and to each add 2 cm^3 of Fehling's solution. Boil each tube for 2 minutes. A positive result is given by the appearance of red copper(I) oxide. Note the time of appearance of the red colour. Repeat using sucrose that has been treated with 1 cm^3 of concentrated sulphuric acid and neutralised with sodium carbonate. (Add carbonate until the solution no longer bubbles.)

Discussion: This test is one of many for the detection of reducing sugars but is not specific; phenols and aldehydes in general will also reduce Fehling's solution. The presence of alkali suppresses ring-formation of the sugars and the aldehyde forms are oxidised. Tartrate is present to bind the copper in a soluble form to prevent the formation of insoluble copper(II) hydroxide (which occurs when free copper is present in alkaline solutions).

Diluted reducing sugar solutions will give green or yellow colours and an approximate quantitative estimate of the amount of sugar present may be obtained by comparing the colour and amount of copper(I) oxide.

3: Barfoed test to distinguish monosaccharides from disaccharides

Materials: Reagent — dissolve 33 g copper(II) acetate in 500 cm^3 water and filter the solution through Whatman No. 1 paper. To the filtrate add 5 cm^3 glacial acetic acid

Sugar solutions from exp. 1
50 boiling tubes
Boiling-water bath
Stop-clock
20 of 5 cm^3 pipettes

Method: Pipette 5 cm^3 of 1% fructose, glucose, maltose and sucrose into separate boiling tubes and to each add 5 cm^3 reagent and mix. Place the tubes in a boiling-water bath for 30 minutes and note the approximate time of appearance of copper(I) oxide in each tube.

Discussion: The different rates of reaction with copper(II) acetate in weak acid solution form the basis of the test. It is probable that the smaller monosaccharide molecules react faster than the larger disaccharide molecules. Although Barfoed's reagent is weakly acidic the reaction with disaccharides is usually negative or very slow. Monosaccharides usually react within 5 minutes whilst disaccharides take about 10 minutes.

Furfural derivative formation has already been mentioned in the Molisch test for all carbohydrates. The following three tests to distinguish between types of monosaccharides are based on furfural derivative formation.

4: Seliwanoff's test for ketoses

Materials: Fructose, glucose and xylose solutions from exp. 1
Reagent – dissolve 0.15 g 1,3,dihydroxybenzene (resorcinol) in 300 cm^3 of 6 mol dm^{-3} (6 M) hydrochloric acid
50 boiling tubes
Boiling-water bath
Stop-clock
30 each of 1 cm^3 and 5 cm^3 pipettes

Method: Pipette 1 cm^3 of 1% fructose, glucose and xylose into separate boiling tubes and to each add 5 cm^3 reagent and mix. Place the tubes in a boiling-water bath and note the colour changes in each tube over a period of 15 minutes. Record the colours and times of formation.

Discussion: This test is a timed colour reaction that is specific for ketoses. In concentrated hydrochloric acid ketoses are dehydrated more rapidly than aldoses to form furfural derivatives. These react with resorcinol to yield coloured products.

5: Bial's test for pentoses

Materials: 0.1% solutions of fructose, glucose and xylose — dilute the
                   sugar solutions from exp. 1 10 times
               Reagent — dissolve 0.6 g 1,methyl,3,5,dihydroxybenzene
                   (orcinol) in concentrated hydrochloric acid and add
                   slowly to 100 cm^3 water
               50 boiling tubes
               Boiling-water bath
               Stop-clock
               30 each of 1 cm^3 and 5 cm^3 pipettes

Method: Pipette 0.5 cm^3 of 0.1% fructose, glucose and xylose into separate boiling tubes and to each add 5 cm^3 of Bial's reagent. Place the tubes into a boiling-water bath and note the colours formed during 15 minutes of heating.

Discussion: The basis of this test is again the differential rate of formation of furfural and furfural derivatives.

   Whilst hexoses produce hydroxymethyl furfural, which reacts to give yellow/brown colours, pentoses give bright blue colours. The condensation product is soluble in amyl alcohol.

6: Aniline acetate reaction to distinguish between pentoses and hexoses

Materials: 0.1% sugar solutions from exp. 5
               Reagent — to 9 cm^3 water add 4 cm^3 glacial acetic acid and
                   5 cm^3 aminobenzene (aniline) (prepare fresh just before
                   use)
               50 cm^3 concentrated hydrochloric acid
               50 boiling tubes
               Boiling-water bath
               20 of 1 cm^3 pipettes
               Filter paper

Method: Pipette 1 cm^3 of 0.1% fructose, glucose and xylose into separate boiling tubes and to each add 1 cm^3 of concentrated hydrochloric acid. Place each tube in a boiling-water bath and hold a piece of filter paper moistened with reagent over the mouth of each tube. Note the reactions of each sugar.

Discussion: Pentoses, when heated with acid, are dehydrated to form furfurals whilst hexoses are dehydrated to give hydroxymethyl furfural. Furfural is volatile in steam whilst the hexose derivative is not. In this way the filter paper wetted with reagent will produce a bright red colour with the furfural in the vapour phase.

7: Osazone formation

Materials: 100 g solid phenylhydrazine hydrochloride (**very toxic, take care in using**)
100 g solid sodium acetate
1% solutions of glucose, maltose and xylose from exp. 1
50 boiling tubes
30 of 1 cm^3 pipettes
10 of 1 cm^3 pipettes
10 Bunsen burners
Cotton wool
Boiling-water bath
Stop-clock
10 microscopes and slides

Method: Pipette 1 cm^3 of 1% glucose, maltose and xylose into separate boiling tubes. To another tube add 2 g phenylhydrazine hydrochloride, 3 g sodium acetate and 10 cm^3 water and heat this mixture very gently over a Bunsen and stir. When the solution becomes turbid add 2 cm^3 of the hot mixture to each of the boiling tubes containing sugar solution. Stopper each tube with a cotton wool plug, mix the contents and place the tubes in a boiling-water bath and start a clock. Note the times of formation of the osazones. When crystals have formed remove the tubes from the bath and allow them to cool at room temperature. Carefully take a portion of the suspension from each tube and place on a microscope slide. Observe and draw the crystals under the low power of the microscope.

Discussion: Compounds, such as sugars, which contain a carbonyl group ($\rangle$C=O) will react with phenylhydrazine to form phenylhydrazones, these may react further with phenylhydrazine to form the corresponding osazone. Sugars vary in the amounts of osazone they form. Ketose sugars, like fructose, produce larger amounts than do aldoses. Variations in the experimental conditions will also alter the yields of osazones and so it is important when comparing different sugars that the reactions are carried out under identical conditions.

8: Tests for polysaccharides

Materials: 1% solutions of glucose and starch from exp. 1

Iodine solution — dissolve 2 g potassium iodide in as little water as possible, then dissolve 1 g iodine into this solution and make to 100 cm^3 with water

'Zinc—chlor—iodide' solution: Solution A — dissolve 20 g zinc chloride in 8.5 cm^3 water; Solution B — dissolve 1 g potassium iodide in as little water as possible, then dissolve 0.5 g iodine in this solution and make to 20 cm^3 with water. Slowly add drop by drop solution B to A until a permanent precipitate of iodine forms (about 1—2 cm^3 of B is required). Store the resultant solution in a dark bottle, well stoppered

Concentrated sulphuric acid

Filter paper

50 of 2 cm^3 pipettes

30 test tubes

Method: Take a filter paper circle and test a piece with a few drops of iodine solution. Test another portion first with concentrated sulphuric acid and then with iodine. Finally test a portion of the filter paper directly with the 'zinc—chlor—iodide' solution. Note the colours formed with the three tests.

Pipette 2 cm^3 of glucose and starch solutions (1%) into separate test tubes and to each add a few drops of iodine solution. Note the colours formed in each tube.

Discussion: As previously mentioned, the glucose units in the amylose chains are coiled into a helix and the iodine molecules will fit inside the helix forming a blue-coloured complex.

The cellulose fibres of the filter paper do not stain with iodine as the intact structure does not permit the accommodation of the iodine molecules within the cellulose molecule. However, treatment with sulphuric acid or strong ionic salt disrupts the hydrogen bonds essential to the molecular structure of cellulose. The result is that the glucose strands separate and iodine is now accommodated in the enlarged spaces between the rod-shaped molecules giving coloration.

The foregoing tests may be applied to the identification of an unknown sugar. The tests should be written in tabular form and a record kept of the positive and negative results. Further confirmation of the identity of the unknown sugar may be obtained by the use of chromatography.

9: Chromatography of simple sugars

Chromatography is a very useful technique for the separation and identification of very small quantities of compounds. By comparing the migration of an unknown to that of known compounds a provisional identity may be deduced. (See Appendix 2 for a fuller description.)

Materials: 10 sheets of Whatman No. 1 paper
Chromatography jars
1% solutions of glucose, fructose and xylose from exp. 1
100 cm^3 of 10% resorcinol in acetone with a few drops of
concentrated hydrochloric acid added
10 separating funnels
300 g crystalline phenol (very corrosive, handle with care)
Solid sodium chloride
Stop-clock
Spray bottle
Oven at 105°C

Method: Prepare the phenol solvent by adding 70 g of crystalline phenol to 30 cm^3 of distilled water in a separating funnel. To this mixture add a little sodium chloride and shake thoroughly. Allow the layers to separate. After approximately 1 hour draw off the lower layer and use this as the solvent (phenol saturated with water). The funnel may be filled with natural gas to prevent oxidation of the phenol.

Spot the sugar samples on to the paper, dry and place in the phenol solvent. The movement of the solvent is slow and the mixture should be left overnight. Remove the paper and mark the position of the solvent front. Dry the chromatogram and spray with the resorcinol reagent. Warm the paper to 105°C for 5−10 minutes until spots appear.

Discussion: The sugars are located as spots. Circle each spot in pencil and calculate the R_f (see Appendix 2) value of each sugar. The locating reagent is that used in Bial's test (exp. 5).

Projects

Sugars in plants are often stored as starch. It is difficult to demonstrate the conversion of sugar into starch in plants while they are growing in the light as photosynthesis is taking place at the same time. The conversion can, however, be shown in the following way. Grow corn or wheat until the leaves are well grown then transfer the plants to darkness so the leaves become etiolated. Cut 11 leaves near the base and place two each in 50 cm^3 beakers containing 0.4 mole dm^{-3} solutions of sucrose, glucose, glucose and fructose, fructose, and distilled water. Immediately after placing in the beaker cut off about 1 cm of the base of each while keeping the basal ends in the solutions. Replace the beakers and leaves in the dark.

The remaining leaf should be tested for starch by immersing in 95% ethanol in a beaker. Place the beaker on a steam bath for 15 minutes to remove the pigments, then wash leaves in hot water and immerse in iodine/potassium iodide in a petri dish. Rinse off the iodine solution with water and spread out the leaf. A purple coloration will indicate the presence of starch.

After a further 48 hours test the leaves in the solutions for starch in the same way.

During the ripening of fruits organic acids are converted into soluble sugars. This occurs in the later stages of fruit development. Select apples towards the end of the growing season using the diameter of the fruit as an indication of its development stage. Select at least five stages. Individually grind the apple tissue in a pestle and mortar adding 1 cm^3 of water per 5 g of tissue. Filter to remove cell debris and pigmentation that may be present. Test the filtrate for reducing sugar.

By comparison with reducing sugar solutions of known strength a rough quantitative determination may be made or DNSA may be used as in exp. 26. Students may then plot a graph of reducing sugar per gram of tissue against fruit diameter. Note that ripening occurs rapidly and thus large changes in sugar content will occur towards the end of fruit development with little change in diameter.

2 Lipids

Introduction

The polysaccharides (and in particular starch) tend to be regarded as the major food-reserve materials in plants. Whilst this is true of the seeds of grasses and leguminous plants the great majority of seeds store lipids as their food-reserve material.

Lipids are a heterogenous collection of substances which are characterised by their low solubility in water but higher solubility in organic solvents such as acetone and ether. On hydrolysis most lipids yield fatty acids. The simple lipids may be classified into four groups, neutral lipids, phosphatides, glycolipids and waxes.

The major neutral lipids are the triglycerides. Those which are solids at room temperature are known as fats and have as their major component saturated fatty acids. Triglycerides which are liquid at room temperature are termed oils and their major components are the unsaturated fatty acids. Acids or base hydrolysis of the triglycerides yields 1,2,3-trihydroxypropane (glycerol) and three moles of fatty acids:

$$
\begin{array}{l}
CH_2O \cdot CO \cdot R^1 \\
| \\
CHO \cdot CO \cdot R^2 \quad \xrightarrow[\text{or } OH^-]{H^+} \\
| \\
CH_2O \cdot CO \cdot R^3
\end{array}
\quad
\begin{array}{l}
CH_2OH \\
| \\
CHOH + R^1COOH + R^2COOH + R^3COOH \\
| \\
CH_2OH
\end{array}
$$

     Triglyceride   Glycerol   Fatty acids

The most abundant natural fatty acids are straight chain molecules with an even number of carbon atoms (C_2–C_{22}). Unsaturated acids contain double bonds whilst saturated acids do not:

Unsaturated   1,carboxy-octadec-9-enoic   acid   (oleic   acid)
CH_3–$(CH_2)_7$–$CH=CH$–$(CH_2)_7$–$COOH$
Saturated   1,carboxy-octadecanoic   acid   (stearic   acid)
CH_3–$(CH_2)_{16}$–$COOH$

When hydrolysis of the triglycerides occurs in alkaline solutions the process is known as saponification and yields the salts of the fatty acids — the soaps. Potassium soaps are more soluble in water than sodium soaps:

$$
\begin{array}{ll}
CH_2O \cdot CO \cdot R^1 & CH_2OH \quad R^1 \cdot COOK \\
| & | \\
CHO \cdot CO \cdot R^2 + 3KOH \longrightarrow CHOH + R^2 \cdot COOK \\
| & | \\
CH_2O \cdot CO \cdot R^3 & CH_2OH \quad R^3 \cdot COOK \\
\text{Triglyceride} & \text{Glycerol} \quad \text{Soaps}
\end{array}
$$

The use of soaps for cleansing purposes is related to their capacity to facilitate an intimate and prolonged mixing of oil and water. This is due to the negative charge which the soap anion ($R \cdot COO^-$) confers on the small oil droplets. Electrostatic repulsion then prevents the small oil droplets from coalescing into an oil phase large enough to separate from the water.

The second group of lipids, the phosphatides, contain phosphoric acid in an ester linkage. They are soluble in organic solvents. Phosphatides are widely distributed in plant tissues and are often associated with membranes. Lecithin is a common phosphatide; here glycerol is esterified with two molecules of fatty acid and one molecule of phosphoric acid which is also esterified with choline:

$$
\begin{array}{l}
CH_2O \cdot CO \cdot R^1 \\
| \\
CHO \cdot CO \cdot R^2 \\
| \\
CH_2O \cdot PO \cdot OCH_2 \cdot CH_2 \\
\quad\quad | \quad\quad\quad\quad | \\
\quad\quad O^- \quad\quad + N(CH_3)_3 \\
\quad\quad\quad \text{Lecithin}
\end{array}
$$

The glycolipids have glycerol linked to a sugar by a glycosidic link. These lipids occur principally in the photosynthetic tissues and are the major lipid compound of leaves:

R^1 and R^2 are
unsaturated fatty acids

Monogalactosyl diglyceride   Sulphonyl-6-deoxyglucosyl-diglyceride

The waxes are the esters of fatty acids and long chain alcohols and are highly insoluble and unreactive. They occur predominantly as the coatings on leaves, fruits and seeds.

Experiments 10—15

10: Grease spot test

Materials: Fatty acids — butyric, oleic, propionic and stearic acids
Fats — corn, linseed and olive oils
30 Pasteur pipettes and teats
10 filter papers

Method: Place a drop of each of the liquid fatty acids and fats on a filter paper and allow to dry. Note if a clear grease spot is present.

Discussion: This is a very useful qualitative test for the presence of fats. Tissues may be tested by preparing ether extracts and spotting one drop of the extract on a filter paper. Dry materials must be used and the ether extract must be a clear solution.

11: Solubility test

Materials: Fatty acids and fats from exp. 10
100 cm^3 ethanol
100 cm^3 tetrachloromethane (carbon tetrachloride)
100 cm^3 diethyl ether
100 cm^3 water
80 test tubes
30 Pasteur pipettes and teats

Method: Take small samples of each of the fatty acids and fats and test their solubilities in ethanol, tetrachloromethane, diethyl ether and water.

Discussion: The fatty acids are terminal monocarboxylic acids with a straight-chain hydrocarbon residue. The polar carboxyl group is soluble in water whilst the hydrocarbon residue is insoluble in water but soluble in organic solvents. The degree of solubility in water is related to the size of the hydrocarbon chain. Even-numbered saturated fatty acids of less than 10 carbon atoms are soluble in water. All fats and oils are slightly soluble in cold ethanol and very soluble in hot ethanol. Liquid fats are not soluble in water and form emulsions (see exp. 12).

12: Emulsification

Materials: 20 cm^3 olive oil
20 test tubes
Soap
Water

Method: Shake a drop of olive oil in a test tube with 5 cm^3 of water. A temporary emulsion is formed which soon separates out into the two components. Repeat the experiment using 5 cm^3 of water which contains a little soap, and observe the behaviour of the emulsion.

Discussion: When liquid fats are shaken with water the fat becomes finely divided into small globules which are dispersed in the water to form an emulsion. The emulsion with water is unstable but can be stabilised by the addition of soaps. Retarding the separation of emulsions is the basis of the property of detergency.

13: Soap formation

Materials: 10 g stearic acid
200 cm^3 dilute sodium hydroxide
100 cm^3 dilute hydrochloric acid
20 cm^3 2% solution of calcium chloride
20 cm^3 2% solution of magnesium chloride
50 test tubes
20 Pasteur pipettes and teats

Method: Heat a little stearic acid with dilute alkali and observe the formation of a soapy solution. Divide the solution into three portions. Treat one portion of the solution with dilute acid and observe what happens. To the other portions add a few drops of the salt solutions and observe.

Discussion: Saponification of fatty acids yields the soaps:

$$R \cdot COOH + NaOH \longrightarrow R \cdot COONa + H_2O$$

(Sodium stearate is the principal agent in household soaps.) Aqueous solutions of soaps are somewhat alkaline:

$$R \cdot COONa \leftharpoondown_{\rightharpoonup} R \cdot COO^- + Na^+$$
$$R \cdot COO^- + Na^+ + H_2O \longrightarrow R \cdot COOH + Na^+ + OH^-$$

If acid is added to this solution the fatty acid is formed and is precipitated from solution.

The fatty acid salts of metals other than the alkali metals are practically insoluble in water. Thus calcium and magnesium soaps are devoid of detergent action.

14: Unsaturation test

Unsaturated fatty acids and fats containing them will readily take up iodine (or bromine) at double bonds to form addition compounds. The decoloration of Hubl's reagent (containing iodine) is used as a qualitative test for differentiating unsaturated from saturated fatty acids. The amount of iodine taken up indicates the degree of unsaturation.

$$\underset{\text{Unsaturated fatty acid}}{R-CH=CH(CH_2)_n-COOH} + I_2 \longrightarrow \underset{\text{Halogen addition product}}{R-\overset{\displaystyle I}{\overset{|}{C}H}-\overset{\displaystyle I}{\overset{|}{C}H}-(CH_2)_n-COOH}$$

Materials: 5 cm³ oleic acid

5 g stearic acid

5 cm³ olive oil

500 cm³ chloroform

Hubl's reagent − dissolve 15 g of mercury(II) chloride into 250 cm³ of 95% ethanol and dissolve 13 g of powdered iodine into 250 cm³ of 95% ethanol. Mix the two solutions and filter

10 colorimeters and blue filters

50 colorimeter tubes

50 test tubes

10 each of 0.2 cm³ and 5 cm³ pipettes

Stop-clock

Method: Set up the system described in Table 1:

Table 1

Tube	Chloroform cm³	Hubl's reagent cm³	Oleic acid cm³	Stearic acid cm³	Olive oil cm³
1	10	5	0.2	0	0
2	10	5	0	0.2	0
3	10	5	0	0	0.2
4	10	5	0	0	0

Start the reaction in each tube (at 2-minute intervals) by adding the reagent and mixing. After *exactly* 10 minutes measure the uptake of iodine in each tube using tube 4 to set the colorimeter to read 8 on the scale.

Discussion: The experiment shows the addition of iodine across the double bonds of the unsaturated oleic acid compared to the weak reaction of its saturated counterpart, stearic acid. The addition of iodine to the double bonds of fatty acids may be quantified as the 'iodine number'. This constant is defined as 'the iodine absorbed (in grams) per 100 g of sample'.

15: Detection of glycerol

(i) A crolein test for glycerol

Materials: 15 g potassium hydrogen sulphate
20 cm³ glycerol
25 cm³ olive oil
5 g any solid carbohydrate
25 test tubes
10 Pasteur pipettes and teats
10 Bunsen burners

Method: To a test tube add powdered $KHSO_4$ to form a layer about 5–6 mm deep. To this layer add 5 drops of glycerol and then add a little more $KHSO_4$ salt. Heat the tube gradually until the irritating and pungent smell of 1,oxo prop-2-ene (Acrolein) is apparent. Repeat the test with 15 drops of olive oil.

Discussion: This test is given by glycerol, either free or combined as in fats. Acrolein is an organic compound classed as a lachrymator or 'tear gas':

$$
\begin{array}{ll}
CH_2OH & CHO \\
| & | \\
CHOH + 2KHSO_4 \longrightarrow CH + 2H_2O \\
| & || \\
CH_2OH & CH_2
\end{array}
$$

Glycerol Dehydrating   Acrolein
agent

Repeat the test with a little solid carbohydrate and note the odour of sulphur dioxide. Organic compounds can reduce hydrogen sulphates to sulphur dioxide which may be mistaken for acrolein. Even fats, if heated too strongly, will yield sulphur dioxide as well as acrolein.

(ii) Colorimetric test for glycerol

Materials: 25 cm^3 5% α-naphthol
100 cm^3 each concentrated hydrochloric acid and sulphuric acid
25 cm^3 2% sodium hypochlorite solution
15 cm^3 10% glycerol
25 boiling tubes
10 Bunsen burners
Stop-clock

Method: Label two boiling tubes A and B. To tube A add 1 cm^3 of water, to B add 1 cm^3 of 10% glycerol. To both tubes add 1 cm^3 of hypochlorite solution, mix and stand for 3 minutes. To each tube add 4 drops of concentrated HCl and boil for 1 minute. Now add 0.2 cm^3 of the α-naphthol solution and then 4 cm^3 of concentrated H$_2$SO$_4$. *Carefully* shake the tubes and note any coloration.

Discussion: An emerald green colour indicates the presence of glycerol and arises as a result of the oxidation of glycerol and condensation of the product with α-naphthol to give further coloured products.

Projects

Students should be prepared to use the lipid tests described to locate lipids in plant material. For example, the guard cells of the stomata of privet leaves contain globules of lipid. Students may detect these as follows. Make a transverse section of a privet or holly leaf, mount the section in Sudan III on a slide and warm over a flame. **Do Not Boil.** Allow the slide to cool and examine under the microscope. Repeat the experiment with young roots of pea and try to locate the casparian band in the endodermis. Roots of snowberry may also be used for this as the casparian band is not in the usual position. The other major source of lipid materials is as a food reserve in seeds. Experiments related to these may be found in Chapter 4 − Enzymes.

3 Amino-acids and proteins

Introduction

Most of the naturally occurring amino-acids are α-amino-acids, so called because the amino group ($-NH_2$) is situated on the carbon atom next to the carboxyl group ($-COOH$). The general formula, with a few exceptions, is:

$$R-\underset{\underset{H}{|}}{\overset{\overset{NH_2}{|}}{C}}-COOH$$

Table 2 lists the 22 amino-acids found naturally in biological proteins.

The individual properties of the amino-acids will depend on the nature of the organic residue, R; the properties of the group as a whole, however, can be attributed to the existence of the dissimilar amino and carboxyl groups attached to the same carbon atom.

Amino, carboxyl and hydroxyl groups are polar groups, that is groups with a tendency to ionise or to induce ionisation in other groups or molecules. In aqueous solution these groups can enter into dissociation equilibria with water. The general formula for amino-acids might be better represented as:

$$R-\underset{\underset{H}{|}}{\overset{\overset{NH_2}{|}}{C}}-COOH \quad \begin{array}{c} \xrightarrow{OH^-} \quad R-\underset{\underset{H}{|}}{\overset{\overset{NH_2}{|}}{C}}-COO^- \\ \\ \xrightarrow{H^+} \quad R-\underset{\underset{H}{|}}{\overset{\overset{NH_3^+}{|}}{C}}-COOH \end{array}$$

Thus in acid solution the amino-acid is present as a cation, since the amino group tends to accept a proton. In less acidic solutions the

Table 2

Organic residue (R)	Name
$-H$	Glycine
$-CH_3$	Alanine
$-CH(CH_3)_2$	Valine
$-CH_2 \cdot CH(CH_3)_2$	Leucine
$-CH(CH_3)CH_2CH_3$	Isoleucine
$-CH_2$ (phenyl ring)	Phenylalanine
$-CH_2$ (phenyl ring)$-OH$	Tyrosine
$-CH_2OH$	Serine
$-CH(OH)CH_3$	Threonine
$-CH_2SH$	Cysteine
$-CH_2CH_2-S-CH_3$	Methionine
$-CH_2$ (indole ring)	Tryptophan(e)
$-CH_2COOH$	Aspartic Acid
$-CH_2CH_2COOH$	Glutamic acid
$-(CH_2)_3 \cdot NH \cdot C(:NH) \cdot NH_2$	Arginine
$-(CH_2)_4NH_2$	Lysine
$-CH_2$ (imidazole ring)	Histidine
$-CH_2CONH_2$	Asparagine
$-CH_2CH_2CONH_2$	Glutamine

The amino-acid cystine is formed by the oxidation of two molecules of cysteine. It has the structure:

$$CH_2-S-S-CH_2$$
$$H-\underset{|}{C}-NH_2 \quad H-\underset{|}{C}-NH_2$$
$$COOH \qquad COOH$$

Some proteins also contain two cyclic amino-acids

Proline   Hydroxyproline

amino-acid is present as an anion since the carboxyl group tends to dissociate, releasing a proton.

For each amino-acid there is a pH value (see Appendix 1) where the tendencies to gain or lose a proton are balanced and there is no net overall charge on the molecule; that is, there are equal numbers of positive and negative charges. This pH value is known as the iso-electric point and it is thought that at this value ionisation is at a maximum and the predominant form of the amino-acid is the Zwitterion form:

$$\begin{array}{c} NH_3{}^+ \\ | \\ R-C-COO^- \\ | \\ H \end{array}$$

Amino-acids can undergo the reactions characteristic of carboxylic acids. They can also undergo many of the reactions of primary aliphatic amines, thus the amino group can react with nitrous acid to liberate nitrogen, which may be measured. This reaction can serve as a quantitative test for the estimation of amino-acids. A more commonly used reaction to detect and estimate amino-acids is that with indane 1,2,3 trione hydrate (ninhydrin). The reaction occurs in two stages:

(i)   Ninhydrin + Amino-acid $\longrightarrow$ Reduced ninhydrin + Ammonia

(ii) Ninhydrin + Reduced ninhydrin + Ammonia $\longrightarrow$ Purple-blue compound

The α-amino-acids can form complex salts with several heavy metals (Cu^{++}, Co^{++}, Mn^{++}, etc.).

Apart from the reactions mentioned, which are general tests, there are several tests for specific amino-acids which depend on the nature of the organic residue.

The amino-acids contain several reactive points in their structure which allow a variety of chemical and physical linkages. The most important linkage of the amino-acids is that between the amino group of one acid and the carboxylic group of another. This is the peptide linkage and is basic to the build-up of proteins:

$$\begin{array}{c} H \\ | \\ -C-N- \\ \| \\ O \end{array}$$

The product of this condensation reaction is a peptide. Two amino-acids linked by a peptide bond are called a dipeptide; three amino-acids joined by two peptide bonds are a tripeptide. Where a large number of amino-acids are linked together they constitute a polypeptide. Proteins consist of a large number of amino-acids linked together by peptide bonds. Their relative molecular masses vary from about 5,000 to several millions.

Since proteins contain acidic ($-COOH$) and basic ($-NH_2$) groups they can ionise in two ways. Under acidic conditions the amino group can accept a proton and become ($-NH_3+$). Under alkaline conditions the carboxyl group can lose a proton to become ($-COO^-$). In proteins most of the carboxyl and amino groups are linked in peptide bonds and only at the ends of the peptide chains do they occur as free groups and so play a part in buffering. However, inspection of Table 2 shows that several amino-acids, e.g. arginine, glutamic and histidine, contain additional carboxyl and amino groups that are not involved in peptide linkages. These groups are thus free to act in buffering systems.

Proteins may be conveniently classified into three groups — structural, nutrient and enzyme proteins. Structural proteins include the proteins found in membranes and the structural material of the sub-cellular particles like the mitochondria and chloroplasts. Nutrient proteins occur in seeds, generally as small grains. The proteins of oil-containing seeds (castor oil, Brazil nut) occur as large granules known as aleurone grains. Some plant proteins (albumins) are soluble in water whilst others (globulins) are not.

The enzymes are the cellular catalysts responsible for catalysing all the reactions of metabolism and are discussed in detail in Chapter 4.

Many of the specific tests to be described for amino-acids also apply to proteins which contain the appropriate amino-acid.

Experiments 16–21

16: The general reactions of amino-acids

(i) Reaction with nitrous acid

Materials: 50 cm^3 of 20% sodium nitrite solution
10 cm^3 dilute acetic acid
100 cm^3 of 0.1% glycine solution
25 test tubes
20 of 5 cm^3 pipettes
10 Pasteur pipettes and teats

Method: To 2 cm^3 of the nitrite solution add a few drops of dilute acetic acid. Pour this mixture into a tube containing 4 cm^3 of the glycine solution and note the evolution of nitrogen.

Discussion: The amino group of amino-acids can react with nitrous acid to liberate nitrogen:

$$R-\underset{\underset{H}{|}}{\overset{\overset{NH_3^+}{|}}{C}}-COOH + HNO_2 \longrightarrow R-\underset{\underset{H}{|}}{\overset{\overset{OH}{|}}{C}}-COOH + N_2 + H_2O + H^+$$

The nitrous acid is generated *in situ* from the sodium salt. Do not confuse any thermal decomposition which may occur with nitrogen evolution.

(ii) The Ninhydrin reaction

Materials: 25 cm^3 of 0.2% ninhydrin solution
25 cm^3 of 0.1% glycine solution
10 test tubes
Filter papers
10 of 1 cm^3 pipettes
10 Pasteur pipettes and teats

Method: To 1 cm^3 of glycine solution in a test tube add 5 drops of the ninhydrin solution and boil over a flame for 2 minutes. Cool the tube and note the formation of a blue colour. Place a small drop of glycine on a filter paper and dry. Place a small drop of ninhydrin solution on the same spot and dry again. On warming the paper a blue-purple colour results.

Discussion: Ninhydrin reacts with α-amino-acids in the pH range 4—8 to give a blue compound. The test is very sensitive but is not specific for α-amino-acids — certain amines will also react.

(iii) Complex formation

Materials: 200 cm^3 of 1% glycine solution
100 g copper(II) carbonate
100 cm^3 ethanol
Water bath at 80°C
Filter paper
10 of 100 cm^3 conical flasks
10 of 10 cm^3 pipettes

Method: Warm 10 cm³ of glycine solution to about 80°C and add copper(II) carbonate until excess solid is seen in the solution. Filter into a conical flask and add a few cm³ of ethanol to the filtrate. The complex will be precipitated as deep blue crystals.

Discussion: The anion form of glycine ($NH_2CH_2COO^-$) forms a complex with the copper(II) ion:

$$COO^- \qquad\qquad ^-OOC$$

$$Cu^{++}$$

$$CH_2 \cdot NH_2 \qquad\qquad NH_2 \cdot CH_2$$

17: Specific tests for amino-acids

(i) Millon's test for tyrosine

Materials: 25 cm³ Millon's reagent (15% solution of mercury(II) sulphate in 15% sulphuric acid)
25 cm³ each of 0.1% glycine and tyrosine solutions
25 cm³ of 1% sodium nitrite
10 of 1 cm³ pipettes
10 boiling tubes
Boiling-water bath
20 Pasteur pipettes and teats
Stop-clock

Method: Add 5 drops of Millon's reagent to 1 cm³ of neutral or acid solution of amino-acid and warm the tube in a boiling-water bath for 10 minutes. Add 5 drops of sodium nitrite. A bright red colour or precipitate is a positive result.

Discussion: Millon's reagent reacts specifically with phenols to give a bright red colour. The only phenolic amino-acid is tyrosine. If a yellow precipitate of mercury(II) oxide is obtained the test solution is too alkaline — repeat the test.

(ii) Xanthoproteic test

Materials: 25 cm³ each of 0.1% glycine, phenylalanine, trytophane and tyrosine solutions
200 cm³ concentrated nitric acid

200 cm^3 of 20% sodium hydroxide
50 boiling tubes
Boiling-water bath
20 of 2 cm^3 pipettes
Litmus paper
Stop-clock

Method: Follow the instructions given for exp. 18 (ii) (see below).

Discussion: Amino-acids containing an aromatic ring system, e.g. tyrosine and tryptophane, will form yellow nitro-derivatives on heating with nitric acid. Phenylalanine gives a negative or weakly positive result.

(iii) Lead sulphide test for cystine

Materials: 25 cm^3 40% sodium hydroxide
Solution A: 50 cm^3 of 0.1 mol dm^{-3} (0.1 M) sodium hydroxide
Solution B: 20 cm^3 of 0.1 mol dm^{-3} (0.1 M) lead(II) acetate
Sodium plumbate solution: Add 50 cm^3 of solution A to 20 cm^3 of solution B, boil the mixture until the white precipitate of lead hydroxide dissolves to form sodium plumbate
25 cm^3 each of 0.1% cystine and methionine solutions
10 boiling tubes
10 each of 1 cm^3 and 2 cm^3 pipettes
10 Bunsen burners
Stop-clock

Method: Boil 2 cm^3 of amino-acid solution with 0.5 cm^3 of 40% sodium hydroxide for 2 minutes. Cool the tube and add 0.5 cm^3 of the sodium plumbate solution. A brown colour or precipitate is a positive test for cystine.

Discussion: When cystine is heated in strong alkali some of the sulphur is converted to sodium sulphide which can be detected by precipitating as lead sulphide from alkaline solution. The sulphur present in methionine is not affected by this reaction.

There are no specific tests for proteins as such and the tests described below will identify amino-acids or links between amino-acids which are present in proteins.

18: Isolation and examination of proteins

(i) Extraction of albumins from dried peas

Materials: 10 g of dried peas
Coffee grinder
100 cm^3 beaker
Glass rod

Method: Grind the dried peas in a coffee grinder to produce some pea meal. Add about 5 g of the meal to 50 cm^3 water and allow to soak for some hours with occasional stirring. Decant off the liquid and filter it. The filtrate contains water-soluble proteins (albumins) and can be used for the tests described below.

(ii) Xanthoproteic test

Materials: 50 cm^3 of the albumin solution from exp. 18 (i)
50 cm^3 concentrated nitric acid
200 cm^3 of 20% sodium hydroxide
10 boiling tubes
10 Bunsen burners
20 of 2 cm^3 pipettes
Stop-clock

Method: Take 2 cm^3 of the albumin solution and add 2 cm^3 of concentrated nitric acid. (A white precipitate may appear at this stage.) Carefully boil the solution for 2 minutes and then cool the tube under the tap. Now carefully run in sufficient 20% caustic soda to make the solution alkaline (use test papers). On adding alkali a positive test is indicated by the deepening of colour from almost colourless to yellow or from yellow to orange. If in doubt divide the solution into two parts — to one part add alkali, to the other add an equal volume of water as a control to see if a deepening of colour with alkali has occurred.

Discussion: Amino-acids containing an aromatic ring system (tyrosine and tryptophane) will form yellow nitro-derivatives on heating with nitric acid. The sodium salts of these derivatives (obtained by treatment with alkali) are orange-coloured. So proteins containing these amino-acids will also give a positive result. Tyrosine and tryptophane are found in all common proteins except gelatin.

19: The ninhydrin test

Materials: Albumin solution from exp. 18 (i)
10 cm^3 of 0.2% ninhydrin solution
10 boiling tubes
10 Pasteur pipettes
10 of 2 cm^3 pipettes

Method: To 2 cm^3 of the protein solution add a few drops of ninhydrin solution and then warm. A blue colour is produced if proteins, peptides or amino-acids are present.

20: Demonstration of protein denaturation

Denaturation of a protein is the term used to describe the loss of the ordered structure of the molecule (see also Chapter 4 — Enzymes).

Materials: 10 cm^3 of 0.01% dichlorophenol-indophenol (DPIP)
200 cm^3 of 2% bovine serum albumin (BSA) dissolved in
5% sodium chloride solution
30 boiling tubes
10 each of 1 cm^3 and 5 cm^3 pipettes
10 Bunsen burners

Method: Label three boiling tubes and set up as follows:

Tube	DPIP (cm^3)	BSA (cm^3)	Water (cm^3)
1	0.5	0	2
2	0.5	2	0
3	0.5	2	0

Mix thoroughly and allow tubes 1 and 2 to sit on the bench whilst tube 3 is boiled for 30 seconds. Cool tube 3 under the tap and compare the blue colours of the three tubes.

Discussion: It will be found that tube 3 is very pale in colour or even colourless as compared to the control tubes. This is because boiling has denatured the albumin. The resulting loss of ordered structure means that previously concealed groups are now exposed. It is probable that —SH groups are exposed and that these reduce the DPIP:

$$2(-SH) + DPIP = 2(-S) + DPIPH_2$$

21: Biuret assay of protein concentration

In many biological investigations it is desirable to know the amount of protein present. This may be achieved by the Biuret assay.

Materials: Protein solution — dissolve 1 g of casein in 100 cm^3 water (add a few drops of 1 mol dm^{-3} (1 M) KOH to aid solution)

Biuret reagent — dissolve 0.75 g of $CuSO_4 \cdot 5H_2O$ and 3 g of sodium-potassium tartrate in 200 cm^3 water in a litre flask. To this add (with constant stirring) 150 cm^3 of freshly prepared 10% sodium hydroxide. Adjust the final volume to 500 cm^3 and store the reagent in a polythene bottle. Discard the reagent if a black or red precipitate appears

60 test tubes

10 each of 1 cm^3 and 2 cm^3 pipettes

Colorimeters with tubes and green filters

Method: Prepare a series of tubes as shown below:

Tube	Protein solution (cm^3)	Water (cm^3)
1	0	2
2	0.1	1.9
3	0.2	1.8
4	0.5	1.5
5	1.0	1.0
6	2.0	0

To all tubes add 8 cm^3 of Biuret reagent and mix. After 30 minutes measure the optical density of each tube in the colorimeter using tube 1 to zero the instrument. Plot your readings against the protein concentration (in mg) on a graph.

Discussion: Peptides which have two or more peptide bonds will give a violet-purple colour when a small amount of copper sulphate is added to a strongly alkaline solution of protein. The colour produced is probably due to the formation of a coordination complex between a copper atom and four of the nitrogen atoms present in the peptide chains. The assay is quite reproducible but requires relatively large amounts of protein (greater than 1 mg) for the colour to form.

Projects

A number of tests for amino-acids have been described. Individual amino-acids may be examined using chromatographic techniques. Meristematic regions of plants and seeds are useful sources of amino-acids and changes in amino-acid content with development may be followed. Grind material in a mortar with water and centrifuge on filter to remove particulate matter. Spot the cleared solution onto Whatman No. 1 paper and use an ethanol:water:0.88 ammonia (80:10:10) solvent and allow the chromatogram to run (ascending) for at least 2 hours (preferably longer). Remember to use marker spots to identify amino-acids in the extract and take care to handle the paper as little as possible for finger marks will appear as smudges later. To locate the amino-acids spray the paper with a 0.1–0.2% solution of ninhydrin dissolved in 2-oxopropane (Acetone). After spraying, dry the paper for 5–10 minutes at 90°C. Certain amino-acids produce characteristic colours, e.g. proline – yellow, glycine – pink/purple, β-alanine and aspartic acids – blue. Most other amino-acids give a purple colour.

Students might investigate the changing amino-acid content of fruits such as apples and tomatoes as these ripen. Obtain juice from the chosen fruits and centrifuge or filter to rid particulate material. Spot the juice on the chromatogram together with marker amino-acids. The juices may be examined for free amino-acids by precipitating the protein with ethanol. It is suggested that 1 cm^3 of juice be treated with 2 cm^3 of ethanol and centrifuged and the cleared supernatant liquid be spotted on to the paper.

The amino-acid content of plant tissues depends upon many factors, not the least being the mineral content of the soil. Molybdenum fed to grasses (apart from perennial rye grass) greatly reduces free amino-acid content. The effects of various metal ions upon free amino-acid content might be investigated. It is suggested that *Lolium italicum* (Italian rye grass) or *Phleum pratense* (Timothy) or clover be grown in sand watered with nutrient solution (see exp. 58). To the nutrient solution add different levels of molybdenum and other metals (separately). It is suggested that three levels in the range 10^{-1} g dm^{-3} to 10^{-4} g dm^{-3} be used. Grow for 4 weeks and then extract 5 g samples of leaf material with 50 cm^3 of 80% ethanol for 1 hour. Filter and evaporate the filtrate to dryness on a water bath and take up the dried residue in 0.5 cm^3 distilled water, centrifuge and treat the supernatant with 0.5 cm^3 ethanol. Apply equal amounts of the different extracts to paper and, using the solvent given above and the locating agent, identify the number of different amino-acids present and try to estimate the relative amounts by the size of the individual spots.

4 Enzymes

Introduction

Enzymes are proteins synthesised by living cells and are essential to all living organisms as they catalyse the biochemical reactions required to maintain the cell. An enzyme-catalysed reaction is thought to proceed through the formation of any enzyme–substrate (ES) complex, the simplified equation being

$$E + S \rightleftharpoons ES \rightleftharpoons E + P$$

where E is the enzyme, S is the substrate (the substance being transformed) and P represents the product of the reaction. Enzyme-catalysed reactions are reversible and enzymes do not alter the equilibrium constant. The direction of the reaction is determined by substrate availability and other factors.

Enzymes have catalytic powers because they lower the activation energy of a reaction. There are many theories as to how this is achieved. A popular idea is that the formation of an ES complex somehow strains the bonds of the substrate so that it becomes more reactive.

Many enzymes are simple proteins and require no additional factors to show activity. Some enzymes, however require the presence of additional factors before their activity is seen. In many cases metallic cations are sufficient to activate the enzymes. In other cases the activator is either loosely bound to the enzyme (coenzyme) or firmly bound (prosthetic group). Coenzymes and prosthetic groups are often organic components related to vitamins.

A remarkable property of enzymes is their specificity, that is, enzymes will usually catalyse a narrow range of reactions or in many cases just one reaction. The analogy of a lock and key fitting together has been used to explain this property, where the lock corresponds to the enzyme and the key represents the substrate which fits.

Because of their proteinaceous nature enzymes may be denatured, that is, the protein structure may be disarranged so that catalytic properties are lost. Denaturation can be achieved by the use of heat, poisons, detergents and strong acids and alkalis (see exp. 20).

The activity of an enzyme may be assayed by measuring either (*a*) the increase of the concentration of the reaction product(s) or (*b*) the decrease of the concentration of the substrate. It is preferable where possible to measure the increase in the concentration of the reaction product(s) since the substrate may be broken down non-enzymatically to yield other products.

In order to measure the change in concentration of a substance (either substrate or product) it is usually necessary to construct a calibration or conversion graph prior to the experiment. This is prepared by measuring known amounts of the chemical in question and plotting a graph of the measurement against the concentration of the chemical. When the experiment is performed and measurements made, these measurements may be converted to concentrations by reference to the calibration graph.

A progress curve of an enzyme reaction is obtained by measuring product concentrations at various times during the reaction and plotting these concentrations against time on a graph (Fig. 1).

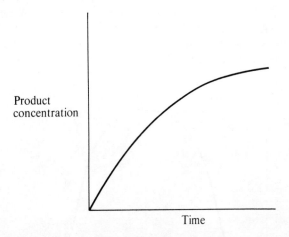

Fig. 1   Progress curve for an enzyme-catalysed reaction

Progress curves of enzyme reactions show that the velocity of the reaction decreases with time. This is due to a variety of factors including enzyme denaturation and insufficient substrate. To obtain a true measure of enzyme activity it is essential to measure the initial rate of the reaction so that interference by these factors will be minimal.

The initial rate of the reaction is measured as the slope of the tangent to the progress curve at the earliest possible time. Experimentally, progress curves are linear at early times and it is not necessary to draw tangents unless the reaction rate decreases very quickly.

The activity of an enzyme cannot be judged solely by the rate of the enzyme-catalysed reaction unless it is known that the reaction rate is negligible in the absence of the enzyme. Thus it is necessary with enzyme assays to measure the rate of the reaction in the presence of denatured enzyme. This measurement is a control and if the control measurement is significant then it must be substracted from the enzyme reaction rate to obtain the true activity of the enzyme. It is also advisable to measure the rate of reaction in the absence of the enzyme. Every enzyme assay must be carried out under optimum conditions and these are considered below.

As enzymes are proteins, their catalytic powers are markedly affected by those factors which affect protein structure. Thus pH will alter the ionic state of the amino and carboxylic groups (and other ionisable groups present) on the enzyme-protein (see Chapter 3). Extremes of pH can also denature enzymes. These effects on the catalytic powers of enzymes (as measured by the initial rate of the reaction) are shown in Fig. 2. Experimentally the pH of reaction mixtures is kept constant by the use of buffers.

With chemical reactions an increase in temperature results in an increase of reaction rate. The symbol Q_{10} is used to denote the average

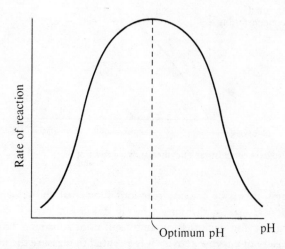

Fig. 2   The influence of pH on the rate of an enzyme-catalysed reaction

change in reaction rate for a 10°C rise in temperature and is known as the temperature coefficient.

$$Q_{10} = \frac{\text{Rate at } t + 10°\text{C}}{\text{Rate at } t°\text{C}}$$

The temperature coefficient of enzyme-catalysed reactions is usually 2 or higher. However, the accelerating effect of temperature increase is countered above a certain temperature by denaturing effects on the enzyme-protein. The temperature where these opposing effects are balanced is described as the optimum temperature, but this is not a constant for any enzyme but will vary according to the exposure time at a particular temperature. These effects are shown in Figs 3 and 4. Most enzymes are irreversibly denatured above 50°−55°C and the activity of enzymes is preserved by keeping the enzyme ice-cold until required for use at a particular temperature.

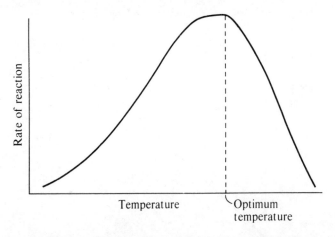

Fig. 3 The influence of temperature on the rate of an enzyme-catalysed reaction

The rate of any enzyme-catalysed reaction depends on the concentration of enzyme. The relation between reaction rate and enzyme concentration is shown in Fig. 5. This linear relationship is found to be true provided that the pH and temperature are such that enzyme denaturation does not occur and as long as the enzyme is saturated with substrate.

A typical curve showing the effect of substrate concentration on the rate of enzyme-catalysed reactions is shown in Fig. 6. This type of behaviour is found when a fixed concentration of enzyme is incubated

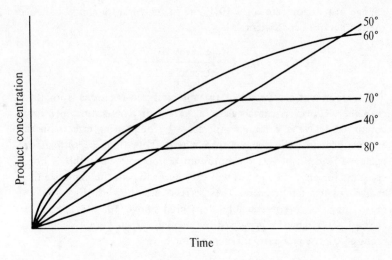

Fig. 4   An enzymatic reaction carried out at various temperatures

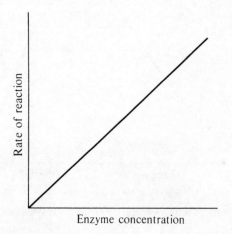

Fig. 5   The effect of enzyme concentration on the rate of an enzyme-catalysed reaction

with a range of substrate concentrations. The velocity of the reaction rises until at high substrate concentration no further increase is seen. This limiting velocity is called the maximum velocity (v_{max}). The substrate concentration required to give half the maximum velocity ($v_{max}/2$) is known as the Michaelis constant (K_m). This is a measure of the affinity of the enzyme for the substrate. The smaller the value of K_m, the greater the affinity.

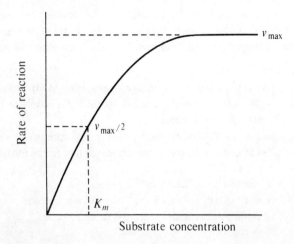

Fig. 6   The variation of reaction rate with substrate concentration

Enzymes in the isolated form are usually unstable and care must be taken to keep enzymes (and unstable reactants) ice-cold before use. Glassware must be scrupulously clean and precautions taken to ensure that the enzyme and reactant solutions are not contaminated with one another. Distilled water should be used for rinsing all glassware after washing and for making up all reaction solutions and reagents.

Experiments 22–33

22: Assay of catalase activity by measurement of oxygen evolved

The enzyme catalase will catalyse the decomposition of hydrogen peroxide:

$$2H_2O_2 \longrightarrow 2H_2O + O_2$$

This is an oxidation-reduction reaction (see also Chapter 5) in which one molecule of peroxide is oxidised to yield oxygen and the other molecule is reduced to form water.

Catalase has a wide occurrence in higher plant tissues although its function is uncertain. It will certainly detoxify any hydrogen peroxide that may arise in plant cells. The catalytic action of this enzyme is such that it gives rise to the most rapid enzyme-catalysed process that is known.

The presence of catalase in tissues may be readily detected by placing small pieces of tissue (apple, turnip, potato) in buffered solutions of hydrogen peroxide and observing the appearance of oxygen bubbles.

Materials: 100 cm^3 of buffered hydrogen peroxide — dilute 50 cm^3 of '20-volume' peroxide with 50 cm^3 of phosphate buffer pH 6.8 (see Appendix 1)

50 cm^3 of 0.01% catalase solution — make up in ice-cold distilled water and store on ice or in a fridge until ready to use

10 each of 1 cm^3 and 5 cm^3 pipettes

10 each of 10 cm^3 or 25 cm^3 burettes with stands

10 boiling tubes with bungs and delivery tubes

Stop-clock

Method: Set up the apparatus as shown in Fig. 7 and adjust the level of water in the burette to a convenient mark. Pipette 1 cm^3 of enzyme into the boiling tube. Add 5 cm^3 of buffered peroxide, and as quickly as possible fit the bung and delivery tube into the mouth of the boiling

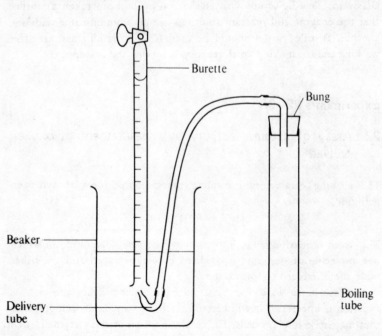

Fig. 7   Apparatus for the assay of catalase activity

tube and then place the delivery end in the burette. On the appearance of the first bubble start a clock and note the time taken to collect various volumes of oxygen. Ignore any bubbles produced in the burette whilst the apparatus is being assembled.

Plot a progress curve of oxygen evolution and repeat this experiment using a control enzyme that has been denatured by boiling for 2 minutes and then cooled.

Discussion: Hydrogen peroxide is marketed as 10-, 20-, 40- and 100-volume solutions. This nomenclature refers to the strength of the solution: a 20-volume solution will, for example, when completely decomposed give 20 times its own volume of oxygen.

With practice the apparatus provides a reliable method for assaying catalase activity and may be used to investigate the effects of various factors on the activity of the enzyme. The strength of the enzyme solution may need to be varied to give a reasonable reaction rate (approximately 2 cm^3 oxygen per minute).

23: To investigate the effect of pH on catalase activity

Materials: As for exp. 22 except that the '20-volume peroxide' is diluted with equal volumes of phosphate buffer at pH 6.0, 6.5, 6.8, 7.1 and 7.5.

Method: As for exp. 22. Note the time taken at each pH value to collect 2–3 cm^3 of oxygen and plot the *rate* of oxygen evolution against pH, e.g. if 2.4 cm^3 of oxygen are collected in 100 seconds the rate of evolution is 2.4/100 cm^3 of oxygen per second. From the graph determine the optimum pH for catalase.

Discussion: It is important to dilute the peroxide solution with the same amount of buffer each time otherwise the substrate concentration will vary at the different pH values. Likewise the amount of enzyme added must be the same at each pH value. In other words, with experiments to investigate the effect of one factor upon enzyme activity all other factors must be kept constant.

24: Assay of catalase activity using a titrimetric method

Hydrogen peroxide reacts with iodide in acid solution

$$H_2O_2 + 2H^+ + 2I^- \longrightarrow I_2 + 2H_2O$$

this reaction is accelerated by ammonium molybdate. The iodine liberated is titrated with sodium thiosulphate using starch as the indicator.

$$2Na_2S_2O_3 + I_2 \longrightarrow Na_2S_4O_6 + 2NaI$$

Hydrogen peroxide solutions may therefore be assayed by adding to them an excess of potassium iodide (in acid solution with molybdate present) and then titrating the liberated iodine with thiosulphate.

$$1 \text{ cm}^3 \text{ of } 1 \text{ mol dm}^{-3} Na_2S_2O_3 \equiv 500 \mu \text{ mol of } H_2O_2$$
$$(1 \mu \text{ mol} = 10^{-6} \text{ of a mol})$$

Materials: 100 cm^3 of buffered hydrogen peroxide − add 2 cm^3 of 20-volume peroxide to 98 cm^3 of phosphate buffer pH 6.8

100 cm^3 of 0.005% catalase solution − make up in ice-cold distilled water and store on ice or in a fridge until ready to use

100 cm^3 of 0.5 mol dm^{-3} (0.5 M) sulphuric acid

500 cm^3 of 0.02 mol dm^{-3} (0.02 M) sodium thiosulphate

100 cm^3 of 10% potassium iodide

100 cm^3 of 1% ammonium molybdate

100 cm^3 of 1% starch indicator

20 boiling tubes

10 Pasteur pipettes and teats

10 of 25 cm^3 burettes

10 of 1 cm^3 pipettes

30 of 2 cm^3 pipettes

Stop-clock

Method: Add 2 cm^3 of enzyme to a boiling tube. Pipette 2 cm^3 of the peroxide into the tube and start the clock. After 2 minutes stop the reaction by adding 2 cm^3 of acid, thus denaturing the enzyme. The hydrogen peroxide *remaining* in the tube is assayed by adding 0.5 cm^3 of iodide solution, two drops of the molybdate solution and leaving the tube to stand for 3 minutes. The iodine liberated is titrated with thiosulphate. Titrate each mixture until a pale straw colour is reached, then add a few drops of starch indicator and complete the titration when the blue colour is discharged. The *initial* peroxide concentration is obtained by adding the acid to another set of tubes before the enzyme and peroxide solutions. The difference between the initial and remaining titres gives the amount of peroxide used (in terms of cm^3 of thiosulphate). Convert the titration values into μ mol of peroxide used.

Discussion: This assay is a more sensitive one than the oxygen assay and lower concentrations of enzyme and peroxide may be used. Note that the method measures the peroxide in each tube. The sulphuric acid used serves a dual purpose, to denature the enzyme (and hence stop the reaction) and to provide the acid conditions required for the assay.

25: To investigate the effect of temperature on catalase activity

Materials: As for exp. 24 together with:

Constant temperature water baths or a hot-water source
Thermometers
100 cm³ of 0.05% catalase solution

Method: Incubate 2 cm³ of peroxide with 0.2 cm³ of enzyme for 2 minutes and assay the activity of the enzyme at 20°, 30°, 40° and 50°C. Since the time of reaction is only 2 minutes it is possible to use vacuum flasks or even beakers filled with water at the required temperature if constant temperature water baths are unavailable. In either case it is essential that the boiling tubes and buffering peroxide solutions are pre-incubated at the required temperatures prior to adding the enzyme. This is to ensure that the reactions are run at the stated temperatures.

Discussion: In this type of experiment it is necessary to equilibrate the reactants (except the enzyme) at the required temperature before starting the experiment. If the volume of added enzyme solution is kept small in relation to the other volumes used it will not significantly alter the temperature of the reaction mixture.

Plot a graph of rate of reaction against temperature and calculate Q_{10} values.

26: To prepare a calibration curve to measure reducing sugar concentration

Two assays are available for the estimation of reducing sugars, a titrimetric and a colorimetric method.

(i) Hagedorn—Jensen method (titrimetric assay)

Materials:

Solution A: Alkaline   potassium   hexacyanoferrate(III)   (potassium ferricyanide). Dissolve 8.25 g of ferricyanide with 10.6 g of sodium carbonate in a litre of water

Solution B: Dissolve 25 g potassium iodide, 50 g zinc sulphate and 250 g sodium chloride and make up to 1 litre with distilled water

Solution C: Dilute 53 cm³ of glacial acetic acid to 1 litre with water.

100 cm³ standard reducing sugar solution, 0.01 mol dm⁻³ (0.01 M) with respect to fructose and glucose — dissolve 18 g of fructose and 18 g of glucose in the same solution and make to 100 cm³

1 dm³ (1 l) of sodium thiosulphate 0.01 mol dm⁻³ (0.01 M)

100 cm³ of 1% starch indicator

100 cm³ of 0.2% invertase solution

200 cm³ of phosphate buffer pH 5.6

100 boiling tubes

Boiling-water bath

Roll of aluminium foil

30 of 1 cm³ pipettes

10 of 25 cm³ burettes and stands

10 of Pasteur pipettes and teats

Method: Set up the system described in Table 3. To each tube add 5 cm³ of solution A. Cover the mouths of the tubes with foil to prevent evaporation and place each tube in boiling water for 15 minutes. Cool the tubes under the tap and to each add 5 cm³ of solution B and 5 cm³ of solution C. Titrate the contents of each tube with thiosulphate until a pale straw colour remains. At this point add a few drops of starch and complete the titration when the blue colour is discharged. The quantity of reducing sugar in each tube is proportional to the difference between the blank (tube 1) and the test titrations. Plot a calibration graph of

Table 3

Tube	cm³ of standard sugar	cm³ of buffer	cm³ of enzyme	cm³ of water
1	0	0.7	0.1	0.7
2	0.1	0.7	0.1	0.6
3	0.2	0.7	0.1	0.5
4	0.3	0.7	0.1	0.4
5	0.4	0.7	0.1	0.3
6	0.5	0.7	0.1	0.2
7	0.6	0.7	0.1	0.1
8	0.7	0.7	0.1	0

cm^3 of thiosulphate difference against mg of reducing sugar present in each tube. Note the relationship between these quantities and the limits of use of the graph.

Discussion: The reducing sugars will be oxidised by the hexacyanoferrate(III) which in part is reduced to hexacyanoferrate(II) which is precipitated as the zinc salt and the hexacyanoferrate(III) remaining liberates iodine from potassium iodide. Solution A is alkaline to suppress ring formation in the reducing sugars (see exp. 2). Solution B supplies the zinc for the precipitation of the hexacyanoferrate(II) and solution C provides the acid conditions necessary for the liberation of iodine from potassium iodide in solution B.

(ii) 2,hydroxy-3,5-dinitrobenzene carboxylic acid (dinitro salicylic acid) (colorimetric assay)

Materials: (DNSA) (colorimetric assay)

DNSA reagent — dissolve 1 g of DNSA in 20 cm^3 of 2 mol dm^{-3} (2 M)NaOH and add 50 cm^3 of water. Into this solution dissolve 30 g of sodium potassium tartrate and make the volume to 100 cm^3 using water. This reagent should be placed in a reservoir such that when air enters it goes through a soda-lime trap to free the air of carbon dioxide (which reacts with the reagent)

100 cm^3 standard reducing sugar solution, 0.01 mol dm^{-3} (0.01 M) with respect to fructose and glucose — dissolve 18 g of fructose and 18 g of glucose in the same solution and make to 100 cm^3

200 cm^3 of phosphate buffer pH 5.6

100 cm^3 of 0.2% invertase solution

Colorimeters with tubes and green filters

Boiling-water bath

30 of 1 cm^3 pipettes

Method: Set up the system described in Table 3. To each tube add 1 cm^3 of DNSA reagent and place the tubes in a boiling-water bath for 5 minutes. Remove the tubes and cool them with tap water and then add 10 cm^3 of water to each. Use tube 1 to zero the colorimeter and measure the optical density of the remaining tubes. Plot a calibration graph of optical density against mg of reducing sugars present in each tube. Note the relationship between these quantities and the limits of use of the graph.

Discussion: Reducing sugars react quantitatively with DNSA to produce a coloured product whose optical density may be measured.

Unknown concentrations of reducing sugars may be assayed by either of these methods and the concentrations found by inspection from the calibration graphs.

It will be seen that although varying amounts of reducing sugars are present in each tube the volume in each is kept constant at 1.5 cm³ by the addition of varying amounts of water. The volume of the incubation mixture to be used will also be kept constant at 1.5 cm³. This means that conditions in both the calibration and incubation mixtures are similar. It is often useful to include a volume of water in reaction mixtures since it may be desired to make other additions to these mixtures, e.g. inhibitors, and this may be done by replacing some of the water by the addition. Thus the mixture volume is kept constant.

27: To investigate the effect of substrate concentration on the reaction catalysed by invertase

Invertase, also named saccharase, sucrase or β-fructosidase will catalyse the hydrolysis of sucrose (a non-reducing sugar) to yield glucose and fructose (both reducing sugars).

$$\text{Sucrose} + H_2O \longrightarrow \text{Glucose} + \text{Fructose}$$

The enzyme is present in the root and shoot systems of higher plants as well as in microorganisms, and will hydrolyse other glycosides which contain fructose.

The reaction catalysed by invertase may be assayed by measuring the amounts of reducing sugars formed.

Materials: Appropriate solutions for the assay method selected
200 cm³ of 1.5 mol dm⁻³ (1.5 M) sucrose (102.6 g in a final volume 200 cm³)
100 boiling tubes
Boiling-water bath
200 cm³ phosphate buffer pH 5.6
20 of 1 cm³ pipettes
Stop-clock

Method: Set up the system described in Table 4, using the stock sucrose solution for tubes 5 to 7 inclusive and a tenfold dilution for tubes 1 to 4 inclusive.

Table 4

Tube	Volume of enzyme/cm³	Volume of buffer/cm³	Volume of sucrose/cm³	Volume of sucrose (1/10)/cm³	Volume of water/cm³
1	0.1	0.5	0	0.1	0.8
2	0.1	0.5	0	0.2	0.7
3	0.1	0.5	0	0.45	0.45
4	0.1	0.5	0	0.9	0
5	0.1	0.5	0.2	0	0.7
6	0.1	0.5	0.45	0	0.45
7	0.1	0.5	0.9	0	0

Start each reaction by adding the enzyme, mixing the solution and starting the clock. Incubate for 4 minutes and then stop the reaction by rapidly adding either 5 cm³ of solution A or 1 cm³ of DNSA reagent. Assay the tubes for reducing sugar by the appropriate method. Prepare two further tubes (*a*) without any sucrose present and (*b*) without any enzyme present at the highest sucrose concentration, and assay these tubes after 4 minutes' incubation.

Discussion: The control tube (*a*) indicates whether the reaction mixture is contaminated by reducing sugars whilst tube (*b*) is used to show if sucrose itself is contaminated by reducing sugars. In this type of experiment it is essential that the reaction is proceeding at a uniform rate when the reaction is terminated. It may be necessary to run progress curves for the highest and lowest values of sucrose to show that the velocity of the reaction is still linear after 4 minutes. If it is not linear the reaction time must be decreased until a linear rate is achieved.

Plot a graph of the rate of the reaction (mg of reducing sugar produced per 4 minutes) against the initial sucrose concentration present in each tube. From the graph determine the values for v_{max} and $v_{max}/2$ and hence determine K_m for invertase. Note that K_m is always expressed as a concentration.

28: Isolation and assay of castor oil seed lipase

Lipases are a group of enzymes that catalyse the hydrolysis of the esters of glycerol:

$$
\begin{array}{l}
CH_2O \cdot CO \cdot R^1 \\
| \\
CHO \cdot CO \cdot R^2 \qquad + H_2O \\
| \\
CH_2O \cdot CO \cdot R^3 \\
\text{Triglyceride}
\end{array}
\quad
\begin{array}{l}
CH_2OH \\
| \\
\longrightarrow CHOH + R^1COOH + R^2COOH + R^3COOH \\
| \\
CH_2OH \\
\text{Glycerol} \qquad\qquad\qquad \text{Fatty acids}
\end{array}
$$

There are a variety of lipases and they may show some specificity for one or other of the three fatty acids linked in the triglycerides. Thus more than one lipase may be required for the complete hydrolysis of any one triglyceride.

These enzymes are found in dormant and germinating seeds which contain fatty oils as food reserves. Castor oil seeds (*Ricinus communis*) are a very rich source of the lipases.

Materials: 100 castor oil seeds
$100 \ cm^3$ of acetic acid $0.1 \ mol \ dm^{-3}$ (0.1 M)
$200 \ cm^3$ sodium hydroxide $0.1 \ mol \ dm^{-3}$ (0.1 M)
Phenolphthalein indicator
20 boiling tubes
Boiling-water bath
Water bath at $35°C$
Measuring cylinders
10 burettes ($25 \ cm^3$)
Pestles and mortars
10 each of $1 \ cm^3$ and $10 \ cm^3$ pipettes

Method: Remove the shells from six seeds. Grind the seeds thoroughly taking care not to inhale any dust as it contains a toxic protein, ricin. This operation is best done in a fume cupboard. Add just sufficient water to work the seeds into a smooth paste. Continue, adding water until the paste is of uniform consistency. Adjust the total volume to $25 \ cm^3$ with water. Transfer $10 \ cm^3$ of the paste to each of two tubes A and B. Add exactly $1 \ cm^3$ of the acetic acid to each tube and thoroughly mix. Immediately boil the contents of tube A for 3 minutes to denature the enzyme. Place both tubes in a water bath at $35°C$, shaking the tubes occasionally. After 45 minutes (or longer if incubated at a lower temperature) remove the tubes, cool and add two drops of indicator to each and titrate with the alkali.

Discussion: The extract from the seeds will contain both the lipases and their fat substrates. As the enzyme hydrolyses its substrate so the solution will become acidic due to the fatty acids liberated. Thus the control tube (A) will require less alkali than the test solution (B).

Ricinolein is the principal glyceride found in castor oil and is hydrolysed according to the equation:

$$(C_{17}H_{32}OHCOO)_3C_3H_5 + 3H_2O \longrightarrow 3C_{17}H_{32}OHCOOH + \begin{array}{l} CH_2OH \\ | \\ CHOH \\ | \\ CH_2OH \end{array}$$

Ricinolein   Ricinoleic acid   Glycerol

The fatty acid is insoluble in water.

Comment on the appearance of the two solutions (A and B) during the titrations and estimate the equivalents of acid produced by measuring the difference between control and test titrations.

The enzyme system in castor oil seeds is interesting in that when isolated from dormant seeds it works best at acid pH (pH 5.0), thus the addition of acetic acid in this experiment activates the enzyme system. In the titration of tubes A and B the solutions become almost clear when the end point is reached. This is due to the fact that the ester of the seeds has been hydrolysed to a fatty acid (insoluble) which is gradually replaced during the titration by its soluble sodium salt.

29: Preparation of crude horseradish peroxidase

The enzyme peroxidase catalyses reactions of the type:

$$AH_2 + H_2O_2 \longrightarrow A + 2H_2O$$

where AH_2 may be a phenol, tyrosine, tryptophane, ascorbic acid or the leuco (colourless) forms of certain oxidation-reduction dyes.

The enzyme is widely distributed in higher plants but its function is uncertain. Experimental work with the enzyme has provided some of the most convincing evidence for the existence of an enzyme–substrate (ES) complex.

Materials: 100 g chilled horseradish root
200 cm^3 ice-cold distilled water
Homogeniser or blender
Muslin
Stop-clock

Method: Cut 100 g of the chilled root into small pieces and homogenise for 2–3 minutes with 200 cm^3 of ice-cold water. Stand the homogenate in the cold for 30 minutes and then carefully decant off the supernatant liquid. Filter this liquid through eight layers of muslin to remove as much of the fine debris as possible. The filtrate may be used as a crude source of the enzyme for the experiments described later. A crude preparation may also be made as above using turnips.

30: Rapid assay of peroxidase activity

Peroxidase, in the presence of hydrogen peroxide, can oxidise both ascorbic acid and 1,4-diaminobenzene (*p*-phenylene diamine). The enzyme will preferentially utilise ascorbic acid before using the dye. The dye when oxidised undergoes a colour change. So with a mixture of solutions 1, 2 and 3 (below) the enzyme will first oxidise the ascorbic acid (without any colour change).

$$AH_2 + H_2O_2 \longrightarrow A + 2H_2O$$

ascorbic acid   dehydro-
                     ascorbic acid

When all the ascorbic acid has been oxidised the enzyme will utilise the dye which undergoes oxidation to give a complex quinone which is coloured. So the time taken for the enzyme to oxidise ascorbic acid completely is given by the time the reaction mixture takes to show colour development.

Materials: Solution 1 — dilute 40 cm^3 of 20-volume hydrogen peroxide to 100 cm^3 with distilled water

Solution 2 — dissolve 0.02 g ascorbic acid in 100 cm^3 of distilled water (prepare just before use)

Solution 3 — dissolve approximately 0.1 g of *p*-phenylene diamine in 100 cm^3 of buffer at pH 5.3

Enzyme — dilute the prepared enzyme (from exp. 29) 1 in 250 using ice-cold distilled water

20 test tubes

30 of 2 cm^3 pipettes

Stop-clocks

Method: Pipette 2 cm^3 of each of the solutions 1, 2 and 3 into a test tube and mix. To this mixture rapidly add 2 cm^3 of the enzyme, simultaneously start a clock and thoroughly mix the contents of the tube. Stop the clock when the mixture shows sudden colour development and note the time elapsed. Repeat the experiment and obtain an average time for ascorbic acid oxidation. The reciprocal of the time taken for colour development is a measure of the rate of ascorbic acid oxidation by peroxidase, i.e. a measure of enzyme activity.

Discussion: The activity of the prepared enzyme will vary and it may be necessary to change the suggested dilution. A suitable enzyme concentration will give the sudden colour development within 20—30 seconds. Greater accuracy in timing may be achieved by preparing a colour standard from a reacted mixture by diluting 0.5 cm^3 to 8 cm^3 using water. Place the colour standard in a test tube next to the reaction mixture under study.

This rapid assay technique may be used to investigate the effect of enzyme concentration on the rate of ascorbic acid oxidation. It is suggested that the enzyme concentration be varied in the range 0.5 cm^3 to 2 cm^3 using the necessary amount of water to keep the reaction volume constant at 8 cm^3. Plot the reciprocal of the time taken for colour development against enzyme concentration (this can be expressed as either cm^3 of peroxidase used or as mg of protein present), and from the graph comment on the relationship between enzyme concentration and reaction rate.

The effect of ascorbic acid concentration upon the reaction rate can also be measured. It is suggested that 2 cm^3 of enzyme be used and ascorbic acid concentration varied in the range 0.02 g/100 cm^3 to 0.10 g/100 cm^3. In this case the time taken for colour development is plotted against ascorbic acid concentration.

31: Colorimetric assay of peroxidase activity

The phenolic compound 1,hydroxy-2,methoxy benzene (guaiacol) is oxidised to a complex coloured product by peroxidase in the presence of hydrogen peroxide. Hence the rate of colour formation can be used as a measure of the enzyme activity.

Materials: 50 cm^3 of 20-volume hydrogen peroxide

50 cm^3 of liquid guaiacol — diluted tenfold using 50% ethanol

Enzyme — dilute the prepared enzyme 1 in 500 using ice-cold distilled water

Colorimeters with tubes and green filters

20 test tubes

20 of 1 cm^3 pipettes

10 of 10 cm^3 pipettes

Stop-clocks

Method: Add 1 cm^3 of the diluted guaiacol together with 1 cm^3 of the hydrogen peroxide solution and 6 cm^3 of distilled water into a test tube. Pipette 0.5 cm^3 of enzyme into a colorimeter tube. Pour the contents of the test tube into the colorimeter tube, place in the colorimeter and zero rapidly. At the moment the needle is brought to zero start a clock and take readings every 10—15 seconds until the reaction ceases. Plot a graph of colorimeter readings against time.

Discussion: A suitable rate of reaction would be 1—2 colorimeter units per minute and it may be necessary to alter the suggested enzyme concentration to achieve this.

There are many other reducing agents that the enzyme can utilise. The leuco form of dichlorophenolindophenol (DPIP) is also suitable and may be prepared for use as follows: Ascorbic acid — dissolve 70 mg in 25 cm^3 of 1% Tris buffer (at natural pH), add glacial acetic acid until the pH is 6.0 and make the final volume to 300 cm^3. Prepare just before use. DPIP solution — dissolve 85 mg in 1 dm^3 (1 l) of distilled water.

To a 100 cm^3 beaker add 1 cm^3 of ascorbic acid and titrate with the DPIP solution until an end point is reached at which the solution in the beaker has the faintest tinge of blue. At this point all the DPIP has been reduced by the ascorbate.

To the solution in the beaker add 1 cm^3 of hydrogen peroxide (20-volume diluted 1 in 1,000). To a colorimeter tube add a suitable quantity of enzyme. To start the reaction tip the contents of the beaker into the tube and proceed as previously described (use a red filter in the colorimeter).

32: To construct a calibration graph for the estimation of starch

Starch forms a coloured complex with iodine (see exp. 8). The more starch there is, the deeper the colour of the complex. Thus the amount of starch present may be measured by measuring the colour intensity of the complex. This can be done by reacting standard solutions of starch with iodine and measuring the intensity of the coloured complex using a colorimeter.

Materials: 200 cm^3 of 0.1% starch
300 cm^3 of iodine reagent — dissolve 2 g potassium iodide in a minimum of water (3—4 cm^3) and into this solution dissolve 1 g of iodine. Make the final volume to 300 cm^3 using distilled water
100 boiling tubes
10 of 50 cm^3 measuring cylinders
10 each of 1 cm^3 and 5 cm^3 pipettes
Wash bottles
Colorimeters with tubes and red filters

Table 5

Tube	Volume of starch 0.1%/cm³	Volume of iodine reagent/cm³
1	0	0.5
2	0.5	0.5
3	1.0	0.5
4	1.5	0.5
5	2.0	0.5
6	2.5	0.5
7	3.0	0.5

Method: Set up the system described in Table 5. To each of the seven boiling tubes add approximately 40 cm³ of distilled water and exactly 0.5 cm³ of iodine reagent. Make the final volume to 50 cm³ with water. Tube 1 is a blank and functions to zero the colorimeter, use a red filter and record the readings for the remaining tubes. Plot a calibration curve of mg of starch present against the readings.

Discussion: A blue solution will absorb red and yellow light but blue light will pass through the solution. Thus blue light is the least useful when trying to measure the colour intensity of a blue solution; red light is the most useful. For this reason a red filter is used when measuring the intensity of the starch—iodine complex in the colorimeter. The calibration graph may now be used in the assay of amylase activity to convert colorimeter readings to units of starch concentration.

33: The isolation and assay of the amylases

The amylases are a group of enzymes concerned with polysaccharide metabolism. α-amylases can hydrolyse α-1,4 glucosidic bonds in polyglycans (amylose, amylopectin and dextrins). The enzyme attacks the bonds in a random fashion and this results in the appearance of dextrins, maltose and small amounts of glucose. α-amylase cannot hydrolyse the branch points (α-1,6 bonds) of starch and so the dextrins are branched in some cases. The enzyme is also named dextrogenic amylase.

β-amylases will also hydrolyse α-1,4 bonds. In contrast to the α-amylases, this enzyme cleaves the penultimate bond from the non-reducing end group of the substrate, thus releasing one maltose molecule after another. This continues until the enzyme comes to a branch point where its action ceases. The enzyme is also named maltogenic amylase.

A good source of the amylases is barley seed. In ungerminated seeds β-amylase is the major enzyme whilst in germinated seeds α-amylases are predominant.

The assay of the effect of amylases on starch may be performed by the traditional spotting tile method or by a colorimetric method. Both methods depend on the reaction of starch with iodine. The products of the enzyme reaction stain as follows: amylose/amylopectin — blue/black; dextrins — violet to purple; maltose — red; glucose shows no reaction.

Materials: Dormant and germinated (48—60 hours) barley seeds
100 cm^3 of 1% starch
Iodine reagent from exp. 32
Sand
Muslin (nylon stocking)
Pestles and mortars
10 of 50 cm^3 conical flasks
10 each of 1 cm^3 and 5 cm^3 pipettes
Stop-clocks
Water bath at room temperature
Colorimeters with tubes and red filters
Bench centrifuge and tubes

Method: The isolation techniques for α- and β-amylases are the same. Dormant seeds are used for the β-amylase and germinated seeds for α-amylase. To prepare germinated seeds immerse the barley in a solution of sodium hypochlorite (1%) for 3 minutes to surface sterilise. Pour the solution off and rinse the grains twice with water. Soak the seeds for 24 hours and then place the grains between sheets of wet filter paper for a further 24—48 hours. The barley should now be swollen and roots visible.

Grind 25 seeds with 10 cm^3 of ice-cold distilled water in a mortar with a little sand. Filter the cream slurry through three layers of muslin (or nylon stocking) and collect the filtrate. If necessary gather up the corners of the muslin and twist so as to squeeze out most of the fluid. Centrifuge the filtrate at top speed on a bench centrifuge for 90 seconds, collect the supernatant liquid and discard the pellet. Store the supernatant liquid on ice or in a refrigerator (5°C) and use as a crude source of the enzyme.

Assay of activity: Prepare eight labelled boiling tubes so that each contains exactly 0.5 cm^3 of iodine reagent and approximately 40 cm^3

water. Then set up the following system in a conical flask (50 cm^3).

3 cm^3 of 1% starch
5 cm^3 of distilled water
2 cm^3 of enzyme preparation

Start the reaction by adding the enzyme and thoroughly mixing the reaction mixture. Start a clock and immediately withdraw a 1 cm^3 sample. Run the sample into one of the prepared boiling tubes. This sample will serve to give the initial concentration of starch in the reaction mixture. Make the volume in this tube up to 50 cm^3 and read its intensity in a colorimeter that has been zeroed as in exp. 32. Continue to take samples at intervals of 2, 5, 10, 15, 20 and 30 minutes from the start of the experiment. Measure the intensity of the starch—iodine complex in each sample.

Convert the colorimeter readings into mass of starch (in mg) using the calibration graph. Draw graphs of (i) starch concentration against time and (ii) logarithm (base 10) of starch concentration against time.

With the small amount of reaction mixture remaining perform a test for reducing sugars (see exp. 2).

Discussion: Graph (i) indicates a rapid initial rate of reaction that progressively declines in rate until no further breakdown of starch occurs. If α- and β-amylases are compared it will be seen that the degree of utilisation of starch is greater with the α-amylase preparation.

Graph (ii) shows that the original concentrations bear an exponential (logarithmic) relationship with time. The reducing sugar test shows the presence of reducing sugars and if these were absent in the original extract then they must have been formed during the enzyme reaction.

Projects

The various factors influencing enzyme activity (pH, temperature, etc.) have been investigated for different enzymes. Using just one enzyme, students might investigate all factors to obtain an overall set of data for the chosen enzyme.

Experiment 28 assays lipase activity in dormant seeds. Castor oil seed lipase shows a shift in optimum pH upon germination of the seed. Students could follow this shift at various stages in the germination of the seeds, e.g. at 6, 12, 24 hours, etc.

The α- and β-amylases used in exp. 33 differ in their thermostability,

β-amylase is more sensitive to denaturation by heat than α-amylase. Students might compare the stability of the amylases to temperature by storing the isolated enzymes at 65°C for $1-10$ minutes and then assaying activity at room temperature.

A great deal of information regarding the nature of enzymes has been obtained from inhibitor studies. As an illustration of inhibition students might investigate the inhibition of invertase activity by metal ions such as silver (Ag^{++}), copper (Cu^{++}), zinc (Zn^{++}), mercury (Hg^{++}), lead (Pb^{++}). It is suggested that 0.1 cm^3 of 0.1 mol dm^{-3} (0.1 M) solutions of the metals be used. In some cases protection against inhibition by metal ions can be achieved by the use of a chelating agent such as EDTA or by the addition of inert protein such as bovine serum albumin (BSA). Experiments might be tried in which the protecting agent, metal inhibitor, substrate and buffer are incubated for 5 minutes *before* adding the enzyme to start the reaction. Suggested volumes to use are 0.1 cm^3 of EDTA (10 mol dm^{-3}) and 0.1 cm^3 to 0.3 cm^3 of 1% BSA.

The hypothesis has been advanced that gibberellic acid produced by the embryo of cereal seeds migrates to the aleurone layer, where amylase is produced under its influence. The amylase then migrates to the endosperm where it converts starch to sugar. The sugar is utilised by the embryo for growth. Using petri dishes containing either starch (1%) and agar (3%) or starch, agar and GA_3 (100 mg) dm^{-3} test all or part of this hypothesis. Students should use half-seeds cut longitudinally through the embryo and then soaked in water for 2 hours. Incubate appropriate pieces of the seeds on the appropriate dishes for 24 hours and then flood the dishes with iodine solution to determine whether starch digestion by amylase (produced in the seed) has occurred.

5 Respiration

Introduction

Respiration may be defined as a process whereby organic substances are oxidised by molecular oxygen with evolution of carbon dioxide and release of energy. The usual respiratory substances are carbohydrates and fats; glucose and propan-1,2,3-triol trihexadecanoate ester (tripalmitin), for example, are oxidised according to the following equations:

$$C_6H_{12}O_6 + 6O_2 \longrightarrow 6CO_2 + 6H_2O \qquad (5.1)$$
$$C_{51}H_{98}O_6 + 72.5O_2 \longrightarrow 51CO_2 + 49H_2O$$

The organic acids which accumulate in the tissues may later be oxidised to carbon dioxide and water:

$$C_4H_6O_5 + 3O_2 \longrightarrow 4CO_2 + 3H_2O$$

In special circumstances proteins can act as respiratory substrates and may be oxidised completely to carbon dioxide, water and ammonia or incompletely to intermediate products.

Many organisms (including green plants) can oxidise organic substances, at least, to a limited extent in the absence of oxygen. This process is called fermentation or anaerobic respiration. The best known example of fermentation is that in yeast which involves the production of ethanol from glucose according to the equation:

$$C_6H_{12}O_6 \longrightarrow 2C_2H_5OH + 2CO_2$$

The original definition of the term oxidation was the addition of oxygen to a substance; reduction was defined as the removal of oxygen. In modern chemistry these definitions have been replaced. Thus oxidation is now described as the loss of an electron from a substance sometimes accompanied by the loss of a positive hydrogen ion. Reduction is the converse of this process. Reactions of the type:

$$AH + B \longrightarrow A + BH$$
$$AH_2 + B \longrightarrow A + BH_2$$

are called reductions of B and oxidations of A. Obviously there can be no oxidation without concomitant reduction and so it is better to talk of oxidation-reduction or 'redox' processes rather than of oxidation or reduction. The general equation for oxidation-reduction can be divided into three stages:

$$AH + B \longrightarrow AH^+ + B^- \quad \text{(electron transfer from A to B)}$$
$$AH^+ \longrightarrow A + H^+ \qquad \text{(loss of hydrogen ion from A)}$$
$$B^- + H^+ \longrightarrow BH \qquad \text{(gain of hydrogen ion by B)}$$

In biological redox reactions some stages may involve electron transfer only, whilst others involve hydrogen ion and electron transfers. In respiration both types of transfer are involved.

Glucose is usually considered to be the starting point for respiration and its oxidation occurs in a number of steps. The first of these steps is common to both fermentation and aerobic respiration and involves oxidation processes which do not require molecular oxygen. It is only in the later stages of aerobic respiration that molecular oxygen becomes involved. A pathway elucidated by Embden, Meyerhof and Parnas, commonly known as the EMP sequence or glycolysis, describes the steps whereby glucose is broken down to 2-oxopropanoic acid (pyruvic acid). Energy is released in this breakdown and utilised to form ATP from ADP and at the same time the co-enzyme NAD is reduced. Glycolysis can occur under aerobic or anaerobic conditions.

The pyruvic acid formed in the glycolytic sequence is further degraded in aerobic respiration by a sequence known as the Krebs or tricarboxylic acid (TCA) cycle. The final products of the aerobic breakdown are carbon dioxide, water, ATP and the reduced form of the co-enzymes NAD and flavoprotein (FP). At this point all oxidations have involved hydrogen ion and electron transfers mediated by dehydrogenase enzymes.

There are four dehydrogenase enzymes involved in the TCA cycle and these remove hydrogen ions and electrons from their substrates and transfer them to NAD in three cases and to flavoprotein in the other case. Thus in the conversion of propan-1,2,3-tricarboxylic acid (isocitric acid) to 2-oxoglutaric acid:

$$
\begin{array}{ll}
\begin{array}{l}
CH_2 \cdot COOH \\
| \\
CH \cdot COOH \\
| \\
CH(OH) \cdot COOH \\
\text{Isocitric acid}
\end{array}
& + \; NAD \rightleftharpoons
\begin{array}{l}
CH_2 \cdot COOH \\
| \\
CH_2 \\
| \\
CO \cdot COOH \\
\text{2-oxoglutaric acid}
\end{array}
\; + \; NADH + CO_2
\end{array}
$$

whilst in the case of the conversion of butane-1,4-dioic acid (succinic acid) to *trans*-but-2-ene-1,4-dioic acid (fumaric acid) the transfer involves a flavoprotein:

$$\begin{array}{ccc} \text{CH}_2 \cdot \text{COOH} & & \text{CH} \cdot \text{COOH} \\ | & + \text{FP} \rightleftharpoons & \| & + \text{FPH}_2 \\ \text{CH}_2 \cdot \text{COOH} & & \text{HOOC} \cdot \text{CH} \\ \text{Succinic acid} & & \text{Fumaric acid} \end{array}$$

The flavoprotein in this case is bound to the enzyme.

The reduced NAD and flavoprotein now donate their electrons to another series of enzymes: the cytochromes. The whole sequence constitutes the 'respiratory chain'. The cytochromes are electron-transferring enzymes. They are composed of haemes; compounds of porphyrin and iron very similar to haemoglobin. The iron present in the cytochromes can exist in an oxidised state (Fe^{3+}) or a reduced state (Fe^{2+}). Thus each cytochrome in its oxidised state can accept an electron and so become reduced to the Fe^{2+} form. This in turn can donate an electron to the next cytochrome. The final cytochrome in the respiratory chain is called cytochrome oxidase and it transfers its electron directly to oxygen. The whole sequence can be represented as follows:

$$\text{Substrate} \longrightarrow \text{NAD} \longrightarrow \text{FP} \longrightarrow \text{Cytochromes} \longrightarrow \text{Oxygen}$$

Cytochromes can accept or donote one electron whereas NAD and FP transfer two electrons. So each cytochrome should be represented as reacting twice. This enzymatic transfer of electrons to oxygen can be inhibited by several poisons among which cyanide is very potent. At certain stages in the respiratory chain the electron transfer is coupled to the formation of ATP by a process which as yet is not fully understood.

Experiments involving such dehydrogenase enzymes require an electron acceptor. This acceptor *in vivo* is NAD or FP. In laboratory studies, however, dyes such as methylene blue or tetrazolium may be used. These dyes change colour when going from the oxidised to the reduced form and so can be used to estimate dehydrogenase activity.

The notations Q_{CO_2} and Q_{O_2} are used for symbolising the amounts of carbon dioxide and oxygen evolved and absorbed. They are usually expressed in mm^3 of gas exchange per hour per mg dry mass of tissue (volume corrected to STP). These values may be combined to give the respiratory quotient (RQ):

$$RQ = Q_{CO_2}/Q_{O_2}$$

When carbohydrates are respired, the RQ is theoretically 1 as equivalents of oxygen and carbon dioxide are involved. When fats serve as the respiratory substrate the RQ falls to about 0.7. Complete oxidation of proteins involves approximately equal amounts of oxygen and carbon dioxide but usually incomplete oxidation occurs and the RQ is about 0.8. If carbohydrates are incompletely oxidised to organic acids the RQ is less than 1. On the other hand oxidation of some organic acids gives an RQ of more than 1; for example, for 2-hydroxybutan-1,4-dioic acid (malic acid) the oxidation RQ is 1.33.

The rate of respiration of a plant or tissue can be determined by measuring (*a*) loss in dry mass, (*b*) amount of gaseous exchange, (*c*) heat evolved. In each case allowance must be made for concomitant photosynthesis if the experiment is made with green tissues in the light. Method (*a*) is inaccurate and can only be used for approximate quantitative values; (*b*) is the most accurate and commonly used method; (*c*) has no practical importance.

Rates of respiration may be expressed as gaseous exchange per plant, per cell or per unit of surface area, volume, fresh mass, dry mass, protein or nitrogen content. The latter two units are the more satisfactory if the respiration of different plants or cells is to be compared; but usually respiration rates are expressed in terms of fresh mass or dry mass.

Experiments 34—40

34: Estimation of respiration by loss in mass (half-leaf method)

The general equation for respiration (5.1) shows that for every 180 g of carbohydrate respired 264 g of carbon dioxide is lost from the leaf. A measure of respiration may be found by measuring the loss in mass of plant material in a given time.

Materials: Pots containing bean plants with at least two sets of true leaves
Cork borers (number 6)
Balance
Oven at 105°C
Stop-clocks

Method: At the start of the experiment bore out three circles from the half-blade on one side of the mid-rib of several leaves still attached to the plant. Carefully label the plants and the circles. Place the cut circles in an oven at 105°C for 1 hour and place the plants in the dark for 90 minutes. Now remove three circles from the other half-blade of the leaves and place in the oven for 1 hour. When the discs have dried, weigh them.

Discussion: If W_{1g} represents the average dry mass of a disc at the start of the experiment and W_{2g} that at the end, then $(W_1 - W_2)_g$ represents the dry mass of material lost during the period of darkness. The process of translocation will also remove substances from the leaves and so the value $(W_1 - W_2)_g$ is not a true estimate of the dry mass loss of material due to respiration. The plants are placed in the dark to stop photosynthesis which would result in material being accumulated. This experiment may be done in conjunction with exp. 41 in photosynthesis.

35: Measurement of carbon dioxide release in respiration by laurel leaves

A better estimate of respiration than the previous experiment is to trap and weigh the carbon dioxide released in respiration.

Materials: 100 cm^3 of Barium hydroxide (baryta water) 0.025 mol dm^{-3} (0.025 M)

1 dm^3 (1 l) of hydrochloric acid 0.1 mol dm^{-3} (0.01 M)

Phenolphthalein indicator

25 laurel leaves

20 small screw-top jars and lids

Perforated zinc or chicken wire

10 of 10 cm^3 burettes

10 of 2 cm^3 pipettes

Graph paper

Stop-clocks

Method: Pipette 2 cm^3 of baryta water into the bottom of a jar. Place a small tray of perforated zinc over the solution and arrange two leaves on the tray so that the leaves are not touching each other. Screw the lid on to the jar and place in the dark for 60—90 minutes. Set up a similar jar without any leaves present. At the end of the experiment remove the leaves and trays from the jars and titrate the baryta with acid using phenolphthalein as indicator. Trace the outlines of the leaves on to squared paper and calculate the areas.

Discussion: Any carbon dioxide released by respiration will be trapped as barium carbonate which is insoluble:

$$Ba(OH)_2 + CO_2 \longrightarrow BaCO_3 + H_2O$$

Titration of the control jars will give the amount of baryta present initially and titration of the experimental jars the amount present finally. The difference between the values represents the amount of barium hydroxide reacted with respiratory carbon dioxide. Hence the mass of carbon dioxide respired may be calculated:

$$1 \text{ cm}^3 \text{ of } 1 \text{ mol dm}^{-3} \text{ is equivalent to 22 mg of } CO_2$$

$$\left(\frac{[\text{Control titration} - \text{Experimental titration}] \times 0.22 \times 50 \times 60}{\text{Experimental time in minutes} \times \text{leaf area in square cm}} \right)$$
$$= \text{mg } CO_2 \text{ evolved } 50 \text{ cm}^{-2} \text{ hour}^{-1}$$

As 1 mol of CO_2 occupies 22.4 dm^3 at STP then 1 mg CO_2 will occupy

$$\frac{22.4}{44} \text{ cm}^3 = 0.5 \text{ cm}^3$$

36: Uses of manometers

(i) A simple manometer

Materials: Simple respirometers
Filter paper
100 cm^3 20% potassium hydroxide
Stop-clocks

Method: As the equations in the text show, respiration involves the gaseous exchanges of carbon dioxide and oxygen. The extent of these exchanges can be measured by manometry and titration. A manometer is a device for measuring gas pressures.

The construction of a simple manometer (or respirometer) is shown in Fig. 8.

Gaseous exchange by plant material in the main compartment of the apparatus results in movements of the manometer fluid. The total net gaseous exchange can be measured if water is present in the side tube. Oxygen uptake can be measured if potassium hydroxide is used since this will absorb any carbon dioxide evolved. By performing experiments with water and potassium hydroxide sequentially in the side tube

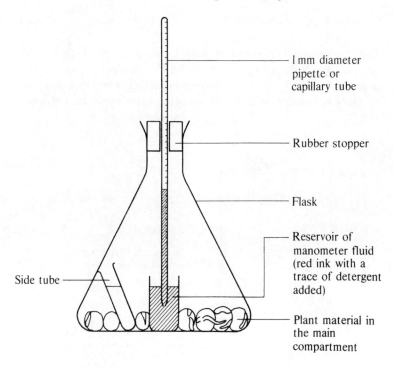

Fig. 8   A simple respirometer

measurement may be made of (i) total net exchange — water in side tube; (ii) oxygen uptake — potassium hydroxide in side tube. The difference between (i) and (ii) will give data for carbon dioxide evolution. Place a strip of graph paper behind the manometer to act as a scale.

Seeds, yeast or small pieces of plant material can be used in the apparatus although if green material is used the apparatus must be placed in the dark to prevent photosynthesis occurring. After setting up the apparatus leave it for 5—10 minutes to equilibrate before taking any readings. If the respirometer is used at temperatures higher than room temperature allow the apparatus to equilibrate with the rubber stopper out for 5 minutes, insert the stopper and allow a further 5 minutes equilibration before taking readings.

The respirometer will respond to changes in temperature and atmospheric pressure and so it is necessary to set up a control apparatus without respiring material to run simultaneously with the experiment and to correct readings accordingly.

(ii) A double-chamber manometer

The fluctuations in manometer fluid level caused by changes in temperature and atmospheric pressure with the simple manometer can be largely overcome by the use of a double-chambered respirometer.

The construction of such a double-chambered apparatus is shown in Fig. 9.

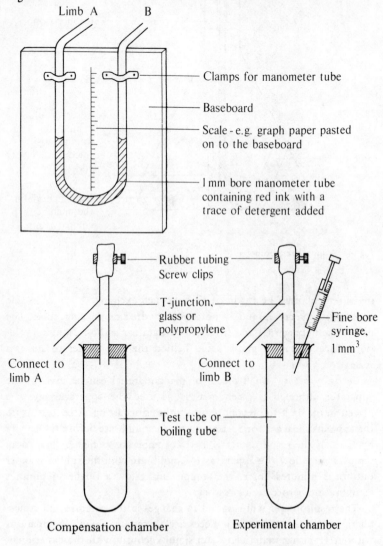

Limb A   B

— Clamps for manometer tube

— Baseboard

— Scale - e.g. graph paper pasted on to the baseboard

— 1 mm bore manometer tube containing red ink with a trace of detergent added

— Rubber tubing
Screw clips

— T-junction, glass or polypropylene

—Fine bore syringe, 1 mm³

Connect to limb A

Connect to limb B

— Test tube or boiling tube

Compensation chamber   Experimental chamber

Fig. 9   Component parts of a double-chambered respirometer

By having two chambers of equal volumes on either side of the manometer, alterations of gas pressure caused by fluctuations of temperature and or pressure during the course of the experiment are applied to both sides of the manometer and so are cancelled. Such monometers are available commercially.

Materials: 10% yeast suspension in 10% sucrose
Respirometers
Water bath at 25°C
Stop-clocks
Measuring cylinders

Method: Set up a respirometer with the experimental chamber containing 30 cm³ of the yeast suspension and add 30 cm³ of water to the compensation chamber. Place the apparatus in a water bath at 25°C (keep the manometer U-tube and scale outside the bath). Allow the apparatus to equilibrate with both chambers open to the air for about 10 minutes with the piston of the syringe fully shut. Check that the menisci are at the same height and close both clips. Start a stop-clock and take readings of both menisci at 30-second intervals for 4 minutes. At the end of this time use the syringe to adjust the manometer fluid to its original position. Note the reading of the syringe. Plot a graph of the differences in height between the left and right arms of the manometer against time. Repeat the experiment using yeast suspension that has been boiled.

Discussion: The graph obtained using living yeast should show a straight line indicating that gas evolution is occurring at a constant rate. Use of the syringe allows the calculation of the volume of gas given off by the fermenting yeast. The boiled yeast suspension should not give any gas evolution thus showing that the yeast needs to be living in order to ferment. The only gas exchange involved in fermentation is carbon dioxide release.

37: Gaseous exchange in pea seeds

(i) To measure the gas exchanges of pea seeds and hence calculate the RQ value

Materials: 20% potassium hydroxide solution
Peas soaked for 30 hours in water (barley seeds may also be used)

> Respirometers
> Filter paper
> 10 cm^3 pipettes and rubber bulbs
> Water bath at 25°C
> Stop-clocks

Method: Using a rubber bulb on a pipette, place 7 cm^3 of potassium hydroxide solution into both respirometer chambers and add small rolls of filter paper to act as wicks. Place a perforated zinc tray above the potassium hydroxide and put six pea seeds in the experimental chamber and an equal volume of glass beads or marbles in the compensation chamber. Assemble the apparatus with the chambers open to the air and the syringe drawn out to the 1 cm^3 mark.

Place the chambers in a water bath at 25°C with the manometer outside and allow to equilibrate for 10 minutes. Close the tubes and start a stop-clock and take readings of both menisci at 2-minute intervals for about 20 minutes. If the manometer fluid nears the end of the scale on one side restore it to its original position using the syringe and note the new reading.

After 20 minutes replace the potassium hydroxide with water and use the apparatus to obtain a further set of readings. At the end of the experiment remove the seeds and weigh them. Plot graphs of the gas exchange against time and calculate the total volumes of gas exchanged. Express your results in the form: mm^3 gas mg^{-1} tissues hour^{-1}.

Discussion: The readings obtained with potassium hydroxide present give a measure of the oxygen uptake since the hydroxide will remove any carbon dioxide that is produced. The readings obtained in the absence of potassium hydroxide give the net amount of gas exchange. If the volume of carbon dioxide produced is equal to the volume of oxygen absorbed then the manometer will not change.

Sample calculation

Respirometer with water gave a production of 0.2 cm^3 of gas
Respirometer with potassium hydroxide consumed 0.6 cm^3 of gas
Oxygen uptake is equal to 0.6 cm^3
(Carbon dioxide produced−Oxygen absorbed) is equal to 0.2 cm^3
Therefore carbon dioxide produced is equal to (0.6 + 0.2) equals 0.8 cm^3
The Respiratory Quotient (RQ) equals:

(Volume of carbon dioxide produced/Volume of oxygen absorbed)
So RQ using the above data would be equal to 0.8/0.6 equals 1.33

The volumes used to calculate the RQ value must be in the same units, i.e. expressed as mm^3 mg^{-1} tissue $hour^{-1}$. The calculated RQ value for hexoses is 1.0. Fats have a lower value as do proteins, whilst some organic acids have calculated RQ values greater than 1.0. Thus it is not possible to deduce from a value of RQ alone which substrate is being respired but if RQ values are used in conjunction with other evidence they are useful aids in the study of respiration.

(ii) *The effect of the testa upon gas exchanges of pea seeds*

Materials and method: As for exp. 37 (i), except that the testas are removed from the pea seeds.

Discussion: Removal of the testa from the peas usually results in a greater gas exchange occurring, thus showing that the testa is a barrier to gaseous diffusion.

38: Isolation and assay of dehydrogenases from pea seeds

Dehydrogenases oxidise their substrates by removing hydrogen from them. The activity of these enzymes may be assayed using certain dyes as the hydrogen acceptors. Methylene blue (MB) on reduction becomes colourless (MBH_2). This reduced form of the dye is spontaneously reoxidised by air back to the blue form and so oxygen must be excluded from a system in which this dye as the hydrogen acceptor. This can be done by using either (i) Thunberg tubes (Fig. 10) or (ii) a layer of oil on the surface of the solution.

$$\text{Substrate + MB} \xrightarrow{\text{dehydrogenase}} \text{Oxidised substrate + } MBH_2$$

Materials: 200 cm^3 of buffered sucrose — take 200 cm^3 of phosphate buffer pH 7.2 and dissolve 25 g of sucrose into the buffer (see Appendix 1)

100 cm^3 of 0.01% methylene blue made up in buffer pH 7.2

100 cm^3 of 0.1 $mol\,dm^{-3}$ (0.1 M) glucose

100 cm^3 of 0.1 $mol\,dm^{-3}$ (0.1 M) sodium succinate

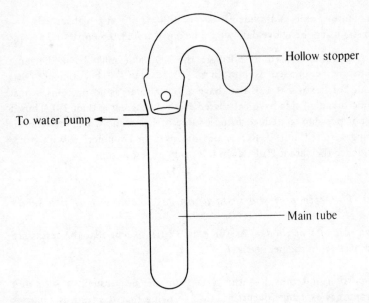

Fig. 10   The Thunberg tube

100 cm^3 of 0.1 mol dm^{-3} (0.1 M) ethanol — add 0.6 cm^3
  ethanol to final volume with water
500 pea seeds soaked in water for 24 hours and another
  500 soaked for 60 hours
10 pestles and mortars
Muslin (nylon stocking)
Sand
Bench centrifuge and tubes
Thunberg tubes or 100 test tubes
Water pump (if using Thunberg tubes)
Paraffin oil (if using test tubes)
20 each of 1 cm^3 and 2 cm^3 pipettes
10 of 50 cm^3 measuring cylinders
Stop-clocks

Method: To extract the dehydrogenases grind 15 pea seeds with
15 cm^3 of chilled buffered sucrose with a little sand in a mortar. Filter
the extract through some muslin and centrifuge the filtrate for a
minute. Use the supernatant liquid as a source of the dehydrogenases.
  Set up the system described in Table 6, using Thunberg tubes or test
tubes.

Table 6

Tube number	1	2	3	4
Extract (cm^3)	2	2	2	2
Methylene blue (cm^3)	1	1	1	1
Glucose (cm^3)	1	0	0	0
Sodium succinate (cm^3)	0	1	0	0
Ethanol (cm^3)	0	0	1	0
Water (cm^3)	0	0	0	1

If using Thunberg tubes place the extract in the hollow stopper and the other solutions in the main tube. Evacuate the tubes for a minute using the water pump, seal the tubes and then disconnect from the pump. Start the reactions by mixing the extract with the other solutions and note the time for the dye in each tube to decolorise.

If test tubes are used add the extract last and thoroughly mix the contents of the tubes and start a clock. Add a thin layer of oil to the surface of each tube to exclude oxygen and note the time for the dye to decolorise.

Repeat the experiment so that data are available for the two types of peas prepared.

Discussion: The various substrates added are used to indicate whether their dehydrogenases are present. The tube with water added indicates the level of endogenous substrates in the peas. Generally the peas soaked for just 24 hours have the glycolytic respiratory system well developed and only utilise the added succinate slowly. However, the peas soaked for 60 hours have had time to develop the aerobic respiratory system (TCA cycle) and are able to utilise the added succinate at a much faster rate.

The experiment may be repeated using yeast and comparing the rates of decoloration between ethanol and succinate.

39: The effect of pH on enzyme activity in respiring yeast cells

Tetrazolium chloride can act as a hydrogen acceptor when supplied to respiring cells; it is reduced to the red insoluble compound formazan at a rate directly proportional to the rate of respiration. Formazan, unlike methylene blue, is not spontaneously reoxidised by air.

Solutions of tetrazolium should be made up fresh and only kept for a few days. Photodecomposition occurs under visible and u.v. light and so solutions must be stored in the dark.

Materials: 100 cm^3 of starved yeast suspension (20%). Starve by aerating overnight

100 cm^3 each of phosphate buffer at pH 5, 6, 7 and 8

50 cm^3 of 0.5 mol dm^{-3} (0.5 M) glucose

50 cm^3 of 0.5% tetrazolium chloride

10 dropper bottles containing saturated mercury(II) sulphate solution. (**Take care — this is a poison**)

100 test tubes

20 of 1 cm^3 pipettes

20 of 0.5 cm^3 pipettes

Water baths at 35°C

Stop-clocks

Method: The colour intensity of reduced tetrazolium is used as the means of assay. Identical suspensions are incubated at the same temperature but at different pH values and the time taken to reach a standard colour is used as a measure of the rate of respiration.

Preparation of standard colour tube:

Set up the system described below:

1 cm^3 yeast suspension

1 cm^3 phosphate buffer at pH 7

0.5 cm^3 of glucose 0.5 mol dm^{-3} (0.5 M)

0.5 cm^3 tetrazolium chloride (0.5%)

Thoroughly mix the contents of this tube and incubate at 35°C until the contents have a definite pink colour. Cool the tube under a tap and add 2 drops of saturated mercury(II) sulphate solution. Put the tube in a rack and use it as a colour standard.

Set up the following system using test tubes:

	Tube number						
	1	2	3	4	5	6	7
Yeast suspension	Add 1 cm^3 to all the tubes						
1 cm^3 buffer at pH	5.0	5.5	6.0	6.5	7.0	7.5	8.0
0.5 cm^3 glucose	Add to all the tubes						
0.5 cm^3 tetrazolium	Add to all the tubes						

Make all the additions except the tetrazolium chloride solution.

Place all the tubes in a water bath at 35°C and allow to attain the bath temperature (about 10 minutes). Time each tube from the addition of the tetrazolium until the time when they reach the standard colour. Plot a graph of reaction rate (time^{-1}) against pH.

Discussion: The yeast suspension is starved so that endogenous substrates of the dehydrogenases will be at very low levels. The addition of the mercury(II) sulphate stops the reduction of the tetrazolium as heavy metal ions poison the respiratory enzymes and so the standard tube will remain a constant colour. In determining the optimum pH value for the reaction bear in mind that the tetrazolium chloride is a salt of a weak base and that its degree of ionisation will therefore vary with pH.

40: Detection of the sites of respiratory activity in living bean seedlings

Materials: 10 broad bean seeds
10 broad bean seedlings (1-week old)
250 cm^3 of 0.5% tetrazolium chloride
20 petri dishes
10 razor blades

Method: Halve a broad bean seedling longitudinally. Boil one-half in water for 3 minutes and then lay the two halves in the solution of tetrazolium. Note the distribution of colour.

Repeat the experiment with the week-old seedlings, taking care to bisect the delicate plumule and radicle from apex to base. Again note the number of respiring sites and the tissue distribution.

Projects

No experiments have been described using inhibitors of respiration. The use of such compounds has been of great value in the elucidation of the pathways involved in the breakdown of glucose. Many of these inhibitors are, in a pure form, costly to obtain and possibly outside the budget of many laboratories. For this reason such experiments have not been formally included. Students however might still attempt some work in this respect. Many marketed herbicides contain respiratory inhibitors. In some cases this seems to be the main phytotoxic effect of these compounds. Such materials are cheap and easy to obtain. They do however come under a variety of brand names though in the UK at least the manufacturers are required to specify content on the packages. The following herbicides act on some aspect of respiration:

1. 2-trimethyl benzimidazole – this prevents the formation of ATP.
2. phenyl carbamates – these inhibit dehydrogenase activity.
3. Atrazine or Simazine – these are inhibitors of substrate level oxidation.

Experiment 35 describes a method of assaying dehydrogenase activity. Make up a tube containing extract, methylene blue and glucose and add a weak solution of the carbamate herbicide (1 cm^3). Since the amount of carbamate present in the herbicide will vary according to the brand, it may be necessary to experiment with various herbicide concentrations.

Warning
These inhibitors work just as efficiently in animal tissues as in plant tissues. They should therefore be handled with great care. Avoid skin contact or inhaling of powders and do not pipette the solutions by mouth.

Experiment 37 describes a method for determining the RQ of pea seeds. This is a starch-storing seed. The experiment may be repeated using seeds of castor (*Ricinus*) which has a large lipid reserve. Compare the RQ with that of pea seeds. It should be nearer to 0.7 than 1.0 which the peas should show. The castor seed has a hard seed coat and this should be broken or removed first. Though seeds are used in these methods fruit material may be used instead. Respiratory substrates change during ripening of fruits such as apple and this change might be followed using segments of the appropriate size.

The effect of environmental factors on respiration is illustrated in exp. 37 which investigates the effect of pH. At the optimum pH the effect of temperature may likewise be studied. It is suggested that temperatures between 15° and 45°C are used.

During the ripening of fruits organic acids are converted into soluble sugars. Select apples at different stages of development and grind the tissues using 1 cm^3 of 70% ethanol for every g of tissue. Filter to remove cell debris. Monitor the levels of organic acids using chromatography. The solvent used in ascending chromatography should be *n*-butyl formate:formic acid (98%):water (100:40:10). Add 0.5 g sodium formate to each 100 cm^3 of solvent prepared and sufficient solid bromophenol blue to turn the solvent a pale orange colour. Run the chromatogram overnight and use marker organic acids to identify the spots. Dry the paper in a fume cupboard and hold the dried paper over a bottle of ammonium hydroxide to obtain better development. The soluble sugars in the apples may also be determined by chromatography.

6 Photosynthesis

Introduction

Photosynthesis may be defined simply as the manufacture of organic material from carbon dioxide and water by green plants in the light. This process involves the transformation of light energy to chemical energy. Photosynthesis is of fundamental importance to all life since it is the major process producing substances of high chemical energy. It has been estimated that more than 100,000 million tons of carbohydrate are made annually by photosynthesis. Concomitant with this carbohydrate production is the evolution of oxygen. The process may be represented as

$$CO_2 + H_2O \xrightarrow[\text{Chlorophyll}]{\text{Light}} (CH_2O) + O_2 \tag{6.1}$$

where (CH_2O) represents organic material which may be starch or some other carbohydrate. If a hexose sugar is formed the familiar equation for photosynthesis may be written

$$6CO_2 + 6H_2O \longrightarrow C_6H_{12}O_6 + 6O_2 \tag{6.2}$$

Chromotographic and isotopic labelling experiments show that a variety of compounds are formed initially in photosynthesis and that starch is in fact a later product. Among the compounds formed initially are trioses, tetroses, pentoses and hexoses, not as the free sugars but as the phosphates of these sugars.

Photosynthesis takes place in special organs of the plant called chloroplasts. These organs contain the photosynthetic pigments which are necessary to absorb light energy prior to its transformation to chemical energy. The major pigments include chlorophyll a, chlorophyll b and the carotenoids. Pigments other than chlorophyll a are often called accessory pigments. Chlorophyll is the main pigment used to absorb light energy. The accessory pigments however will absorb light and may transfer the absorbed energy to chlorophyll. The main accessory pigments that service chlorophyll in this way are β-carotene, xanthophyll, phycocyanins and phycoerythrin. The presence of these pigments may be demonstrated by chromatographic techniques.

In studying the physiology of any plant process the first object is to find the conditions necessary for the attainment of the maximum rate. Thus variations in light intensity, carbon dioxide concentration and temperature will all affect the rate of photosynthesis. The rate of a complete process will be governed or limited by the rate of the slowest constituent reaction. Experiments have shown however that photosynthesis is not limited by any single factor but rather by an interaction of factors. Thus for a given light intensity there is a concentration of carbon dioxide at which all the light energy is being used and increasing the carbon dioxide concentration has no effect upon the photosynthetic rate. However, upon using higher light intensities the rate may be increased (Fig. 11). Thus the interaction of light intensity and carbon dioxide concentration are affecting the rate of photosynthesis.

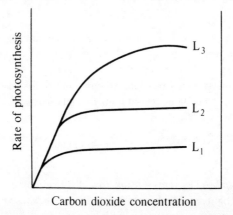

Fig. 11   The effects of carbon dioxide concentration, at different light intensities (L_1, L_2 and L_3) on the rate of photosynthesis

Bearing this interaction of factors in mind it will be seen that the study of variation of one factor is simplified if all other factors are kept at a chosen constant level, preferably at optimal level.

If the rate of photosynthesis is examined under various light intensities and temperatures a very interesting finding is made. As Fig. 12 shows, at low light intensities the photosynthetic rate is independent of temperature, i.e. Q_{10} is 1 (see also Chapter 5). At higher light intensities photosynthesis is affected by temperature and the Q_{10} is 2 or higher. A Q_{10} of 1 is indicative of a photochemical reaction whilst a Q_{10} of 2 or higher indicates a chemical reaction. These results (and others) lead to

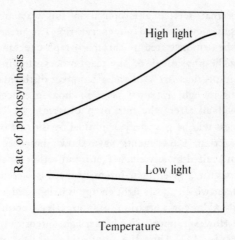

Fig. 12   The effect of light intensity at different temperatures on the rate of photosynthesis

the idea that photosynthesis consists of two main stages. The first involves the absorption of light by chlorophyll and its conversion to chemical energy and is called the light reaction. The second stage involves the utilisation of this chemical energy to reduce carbon dioxide in a dark reaction. The light reaction may be summarised as

$$NADP + ADP + P_{INORGANIC} + H_2O \xrightarrow[\text{Chlorophyll}]{\text{Light}} NADPH + ATP + O_2$$

(6.3)

The NADPH and ATP, representing the chemical energy obtained by conversion of light energy by chlorophyll, are now used in the dark reaction:

$$NADPH + ATP + CO_2 \longrightarrow (CH_2O) + ADP + P_{INORGANIC} + NADP$$

(6.4)

As might be inferred from equations (6.3) and (6.4) the oxygen evolved in photosynthesis is derived from water and not carbon dioxide. This has been verified in experiments using water labelled with the isotope O^{18}. The oxygen evolved in these experiments contained the same concentration of O^{18} as the water. So photosynthesis is better represented as:

$$CO_2 + 2H_2O^{18} \xrightarrow[\text{Chlorophyll}]{\text{Light}} (CH_2O) + H_2O + O_2^{18}$$

with water appearing on both sides of the equation to indicate that the oxygen evolved in derived from water. Photosynthesis may thus be defined as an oxidation—reduction reaction (see Chapter 5) in which carbon dioxide is reduced to organic material whilst water is oxidised to oxygen. The energy necessary to drive this reaction is supplied by light. As in respiration, cytochromes are involved in this redox process and ATP is thought to be formed by a similar mechanism, but as yet the details are not fully known.

Much information concerning photosynthesis has been derived from studies with isolated chloroplasts. In 1937 R. Hill showed that chloroplasts, when freed from other cell contents and illuminated, can reduce certain reagents and produce oxygen. Carbon dioxide was not reduced in these reactions which are now named after Hill. A variety of substances, some natural, others not, can be reduced in this reaction and such substances are known as Hill reagents. Among the most reactive Hill reagents are hexacyanoferrate(III), NADP and a variety of dyes:

$$2A + 2H_2O \xrightarrow[\text{Chlorophyll}]{\text{Light}} 2AH_2 + O_2$$

Since the work of Hill several workers have shown that isolated chloroplasts under special conditions can reduce carbon dioxide to carbohydrates. Thus carbon dioxide is a Hill reagent of special physiological importance. The Hill reaction is a very important mechanism which shows many similarities to photosynthesis in the intact plant.

As the equations show, photosynthesis involves the uptake of carbon dioxide, the evolution of oxygen and the production of carbohydrates. So the measurement of photosynthesis in plants can be made either by monitoring gas exchanges or changes in the dry mass of plants. In either case a correction must be made for the concomitant respiration occurring (with its gas exchanges opposite to those of photosynthesis). In very bright light the rate of photosynthesis may be as much as 100 times more rapid than that of respiration so that the correction is of small importance. However, at low light intensities photosynthesis and respiration occur at more nearly equal rates and the extent of respiration must be considered. The point where the two processes balance each other is known as the 'compensation point'. The excess of photosynthesis over respiration is often referred to as 'net assimilation'.

Rates of photosynthesis may be expressed per plant, per unit of surface area, fresh mass, dry mass, nitrogen content, protein or chlorophyll content. When calculated on a fresh mass basis, lower values are obtained for land plants than for algae. Most of this difference is attributable to the smaller percentage of photosynthetic cells in the vascular plants.

In measurements of gaseous exchange a figure, the 'assimilatory quotient' (AQ), is often used. This represents the ratio of CO_2 absorbed/O_2 evolved. When carbohydrates are the main products of photosynthesis AQ is 1. If fats and proteins are accumulated to any extent the AQ is less than 1.

The equation (6.2) in the text for photosynthesis shows that, apart from the gas exchanges, 180 g of carbohydrate is photosynthesised from 264 g of carbon dioxide and 108 g of water. A measure of the amount of photosynthesis may be found by determining the dry mass changes occurring in green leaves during a period of illumination.

Experiments 41—47

41: Sach's half-leaf method for measuring photosynthesis

Materials: Pots containing bean plants with at least two sets of true leaves (place the plants in the dark for 12 or more hours prior to starting the experiment)
Cork borers (number 6)
Lights — photoflood lamps or 150 W bulbs
Balances
Oven at 105°C
Stop-clocks

Method: At the start of the experiment bore out three circles from the half-blade on one side of the mid-rib of several leaves still attached to the plant (avoiding as far as possible any large veins). Carefully label the plants and circles. Place the cut circles in an oven at 105°C for 1 hour. Illuminate the plants for 90 minutes, taking care, by placing a battery jar or beaker filled with water between the lamp and the plant, to avoid heating the plants. After 90 minutes remove three circles from the intact half-blades of the leaves and place in the oven for 1 hour. When the discs have dried, weigh them. At the same time repeat the experiment for some plants that have been kept in the dark for 90 minutes.

Discussion: If W_{1g} is the average dry mass of a disc at the start of the experiment and W_{2g} that at the end, then $(W_2 - W_1)_g$ represents the dry mass of material accumulated during the period of illumination. However, other physiological processes such as respiration and translocation will remove materials from the leaves and so the mass will change. This is corrected by using the samples kept in the dark for 90 minutes. Determine their average loss in dry mass $(W_3 - W_4)_g$. The average amount of dry material formed by photosynthesis per disc is given by $(W_2 - W_1)_g + (W_3 - W_4)_g$. This result is expressed as g increase in dry mass per cm^2 of leaf surface. This experiment may be done in conjunction with exp. 34.

The following experiments (42–44) investigate the effects of varying certain external factors on the rate of photosynthesis and are used to determine the optimal conditions for photosynthesis.

The general equation (6.2) for photosynthesis shows how carbon dioxide and oxygen exchanges occur. An estimate of the rate of the process may be gained by measuring the pressure changes due either to carbon dioxide uptake or to oxygen evolution. A manometer is a device for measuring gas pressures and the use of a double-chamber manometer is described in exp. 36 (ii).

As photosynthesis proceeds the concentration of carbon dioxide falls. However, the concentration of carbon dioxide around an aquatic plant can be kept constant without causing a change in pressure in a closed system such as the manometer by placing the plant in a hydrogen carbonate acid salt solution. As the cells photosynthesise and use carbon dioxide so more of the gas is provided by the hydrogen carbonate. Since the carbon dioxide concentration in the gas phase does not change only the pressure change due to oxygen production is measured. So the rate of photosynthesis may be gauged by this pressure change.

General method: Add a sprig of Elodea to the experimental chamber and fill two-thirds full with hydrogen carbonate solution. Fill the compensation chamber to the same level with hydrogen carbonate. Place the chambers in a beaker at the required temperature and allow to equilibrate for 10 minutes making sure the screw clips are open and the syringe is fully shut. The beaker should be painted black leaving a vertical slit through which the experimental chamber may be illuminated. Take care to avoid heating effects of the lamp. After equilibration, close both clips simultaneously, note the manometer reading and take further readings at suitable intervals. The volume of oxygen evolved may be measured at any instant by withdrawing the syringe piston until the liquid in the manometer is again at the same height in both limbs. Note the new reading of the syringe each time this is done.

42: To investigate the effect of light intensity upon the rate of photosynthesis

Materials: Sprigs of Elodea (or any aquatic green plants)
1% solution of sodium hydrogen carbonate
Double-chamber manometers (see exp. 36 (ii))
Lights — photoflood lamps or 150 W bulbs
Large beaker painted black except for a vertical slit
Metre rulers
Thermometer
Stop-clocks

Method: Set up the apparatus using 1% hydrogen carbonate in the chambers and allow to equilibrate. After equilibration measure the change in pressure (mm min^{-1}) using the following intensities:

 (i) Darkness; wrap the tubes in aluminium foil
(ii) Light source at 10, 15, 20 and 32 cm from the experimental chamber

Several readings at each intensity should be taken at 2-minute intervals to give the average rate of pressure change (oxygen evolved) expressed as mm min^{-1}. Alternatively the volume of gas produced may be measured using the syringe as described above.

Discussion: The light intensity at a distance d cm from the lamp is proportional to $1/d^2$ (inverse square law). Plot a graph of $1/d^2$ against the pressure change (mm min^{-1}) of the rate of gas production (oxygen evolved). The tube in darkness will give the rate of respiration (oxygen uptake). If it is assumed that respiration continues unchanged in the light it will be necessary to correct the 'apparent' photosynthetic rates to obtain the 'net' rate. Comment on the factors which are limiting the rate of photosynthesis at the light intensities used.

43: To investigate the effect of carbon dioxide concentration on the rate of photosynthesis

Materials: As for exp. 42 together with sodium hydrogen carbonate solutions of 0.02%, 0.05%, 0.1%, 0.5% and 1% strengths.

Method: Set up the manometer as in the previous experiment and measure the rate of photosynthesis using the lamp at 10 cm. Keep the temperature constant and vary the hydrogen carbonate solution. Obtain an average rate of oxygen evolution as before.

Discussion: Plot a graph of concentration of carbon dioxide (expressed as % hydrogen carbonate solution) against the photosynthetic rate. Compare the results of this experiment with those of the previous experiment.

44: To investigate the effect of temperature on the rate of photosynthesis

Materials: As for exp. 42 together with a source of hot water.

Method: Set up the apparatus and measure the rate of photosynthesis in the temperature range 20°–40°C at two temperatures which are 10°C apart (e.g. 21° and 31°C). Perform the experiment twice, once using a low light intensity and once with a high light intensity. Obtain an average rate of photosynthesis as before (use 1% sodium hydrogen carbonate).

Discussion: Calculate the temperature coefficient (Q_{10}) for both light intensities. Collate the results of exps. 42, 43 and 44 and determine (*a*) the factor(s) limiting the rate of photosynthesis and (*b*) the conditions necessary for optimal rates of photosynthesis in these experiments. Set up further experiments to verify your answers to (*a*) and (*b*) above.

45: Isolation of chloroplasts

Materials: Fresh spinach, lettuce or pea seedlings (10–14 days old)
Scissors
Blender or homogeniser
Bench centrifuge and tubes
Muslin
Refrigerator or freezing mixture
Buffer solution — add 6 g of glucose and 0.01 g of potassium chloride to every 100 cm³ of phosphate buffer pH 6.5 (see Appendix 1)
Stop-clocks

Method: Weigh out 50 g of plant material and cut into small pieces. Thaw 120 cm^3 of the buffer solution until it has the consistency of melting snow. Add this solution to the blender and set the blades revolving at half speed. Gradually add the cut plant material to the blender over a period of 15–20 seconds. When the last piece is drawn below the revolving blades switch the blender to full speed for 5 seconds. Filter the homogenate, first through two layers of muslin into a beaker sitting on ice. Take the filtrate and filter through eight layers of muslin into another beaker on ice. Pour equal amounts of the filtrate into centrifuge tubes and centrifuge at top speed for 2 minutes. Discard the supernatant liquids and place the tubes on ice. Using a total 10–15 cm^3 of ice-cold buffer solution gently resuspend the chloroplast pellets using a fine paint brush or a piece of cotton wool. Store the suspension on ice in the dark.

Discussion: It is essential that all solutions, glassware, centrifuge tubes and head are kept as cold as possible. The various operations should be performed as quickly as possible to retard denaturation of the chloroplasts. Whilst the homogenising process is an inefficient one it nevertheless produces very active chloroplasts. The double filtration through muslin is used to rid the homogenate of the coarse cell debris and is faster than a slow centrifugation step which is sometimes used at this stage in the isolation procedure. Sucrose is present as an osmoticum to stop the chloroplasts from breaking.

If a blender is not available, the green material may be ground in an ice-cold mortar with an ice-cold buffer solution. It is necessary to minimise the grinding and accept a lower yield of chloroplasts as excessive grinding will inactivate the chloroplasts.

46: Investigation of the Hill reaction

Materials: Chloroplast suspension from previous experiment
200 cm^3 of buffer solution from previous experiment (at room temperature)
50 cm^3 of 0.1% solution of dichlorophenol-indophenol (DPIP)
1 cm^3 and 10 cm^3 pipettes
Lights – photoflood lamps or 150 W lamps
Colorimeters with tubes and green filters
Stop-clocks

Method: Set up in a colorimeter tube the following system:

Buffer solution	8.0 cm^3
Dye 0.1%	0.2 cm^3
Chloroplasts	0.5 cm^3

Mix the tube contents and place the tube in a colorimeter with the filter in position and adjust the needle to read approximately 7 on the scale. Remove the tube and begin illumination for 15-second intervals recording the decrease in absorbance after each period of illumination (take care to avoid heating effects of the light). Continue until a constant reading is obtained. Construct a progress curve for dye reduction plotting decrease in absorbance against time. Set up another tube, adjust the colorimeter to read 7 with the tube in position then place the tube in the dark for 10 minutes and then take a reading.

Discussion: It may be necessary to alter the volume of the dye added so that the colorimeter will read on the scale. Depending on the activity of the chloroplasts it may be necessary to increase or decrease the volume. In both cases compensate to keep the volume total at about 8.5−9.0 cm^3 using buffer solution.

The reduction of the dye in the Hill reaction may be represented as:

$$2DPIP + 2H_2O \longrightarrow 2DPIPH_2 + O_2$$

This reaction results in the disappearance of the blue colour of the dye as it is reduced. The tube kept in the dark gives a measure of any non-photosynthetic events which result in dye reduction.

47: Isolation and separation of the photosynthetic pigments

Materials: Spinach or nettle leaves (or any non-waxy leaves)
Blenders or mortars and pestles
Buchner funnels and filter paper
Separating funnels
2-oxopropane (acetone)
90% solution of acetone dimethyl ketone (acetone)
10% solution of sodium chloride
Ethyl ethanoate (ethyl acetate)
Diethylamine
Ethoxyethane (diethyl ether)
Petroleum ether (b.p. 60°−80°)
Petroleum ether (b.p. 100°−120°)

Solid sodium sulphate
Whatman No. 1 paper
Silica gel plates
Measuring cylinders
Balances
Stop-clocks
Fume cupboard
Fine capillaries or platinum loops

Two methods are described, one for use with paper chromatography (*a*) and the other for use with thin layer chromatography (*b*).

Method (a):   Grind 10 g of leaf material with 20 cm^3 of 90% acetone and filter the extract through filter paper using a Buchner funnel. Measure the volume of the coloured filtrate and place in a separating funnel. Add an equal volume of petroleum ether (b.p. 100°–120°) and shake the mixture. 'Wash' the mixture by adding distilled water, shake the funnel and discard the lower aqueous layer. The pigments may be further treated by adding solid sodium sulphate and allowing to stand for a few minutes.

Spot Whatman No. 1 paper with drops of freshly extracted pigment and run the chromatogram in a mixture of 100 parts of petroleum ether (b.p. 100°–120°) and 12 parts of 90% acetone. Run the chromatogram for at least 6 hours and preferably overnight. Measure the R_f values (see Appendix 2) of the separated pigments and correlate the colours of the pigments with their absorption spectra.

Method (b):   Grind 10 g of leaf material with 30 cm^3 of 90% acetone and filter the extract through filter paper using a Buchner funnel. Measure the volume of the filtrate and add an equal volume of diethyl ether. Place this mixture in a separating funnel and 'wash' three times with 25 cm^3 aliquots of sodium chloride solution, discarding the lower aqueous phase each time. The ether solution of the pigments is evaporated at room temperature either by using a stream of nitrogen gas or allowing evaporation to occur overnight in a fume cupboard. Dissolve the pigment mixture in about 1 cm^3 of acetone and spot the solution as a line 1 cm from the edge of an activated Silica Gel G plate. Run the plate in the dark in a mixture of 58 parts of petroleum ether (b.p. 60°–80°), 30 parts of ethyl acetate and 12 parts of diethylamine.

Discussion: The adsorbed pigments are very sensitive to photo-oxidation reactions and it is best to perform the experiments in diffuse light. No locating reagents are required as the spots are coloured. It is difficult to quote exact R_f values for the different systems as R_f depends very much on the conditions of the experiment. However, the order of separation of the pigments is constant and this is shown below:

Paper chromatography:

	Band	Identity
Solvent front	Yellow	Carotenes
	Yellow-grey	Phaeophytin
	Yellow-brown	Xanthophyll
	Blue-green	Chlorophyll a
	Green	Chlorophyll b
Origin	Green	Chlorophyllide a

Thin layer chromatography:

	Band	Identity
Solvent front	Yellow	Carotenes
	Yellow-grey	Phaeophytin
	Blue-green	Chlorophyll a
	Green	Chlorophyll b
	Dull yellow	Xanthophylls
Origin	Green	Chlorophyllide a

The Xanthophylls may appear as two bands. Chlorophyllide and phaeophytin are the products of the enzymic breakdown of the chlorophylls that occurs in the isolation procedure.

Projects

An approximate absorption spectrum for chlorophyll may be obtained by extracting the isolated chloroplasts used in exp. 45 with 80% acetone and centrifuging to remove solid material. Using the acetone extract, measure the absorbance using each colorimeter filter in turn, remembering to zero the colorimeter for each filter using an 80% acetone blank. Alternatively, if the colorimeter reads transmission, set the instrument to 100% transmission with the acetone blank each time a different filter is used. Subtract each reading from 100 to obtain the approximate absorption for each filter. The colorimeter manual or catalogue will give the peak wavelength for each filter. Plot the absorbance against peak wavelength to obtain the approximate absorption spectrum and compare this with published spectra.

In exp. 42 a method is described from measuring photosynthesis. It is based upon the increase in mass observed during the exposure of bean plants to light. The exposure time suggested is 90 minutes. Students might illuminate plants for varying lengths of time and record their results in terms of increase in mass over the controls (see exp. 42). It would theoretically be expected that the discs of leaf would show an increase in mass proportional to the light exposure up to a maximum and thereafter no further increase. This would be attributed to an increase in total photosynthetic products until a point where the rate of photosynthesis is constant for the environmental conditions of the experiment and the rate of translocation of these products has reached a maximum for that level of production. In practice, a proportional increase probably will not occur over short exposures since the increases in mass will be small and the experimental error due to inaccuracies in cutting the discs, drying, and weighing, will be relatively large. Students should be encouraged to reach these conclusions themselves as part of an exercise in critical evaluation of experimental methods.

In the extraction of pigments, exp. 49, tissue is used from dicotyledenous plants. Students might attempt extraction from algae tissue and compare the pigments. Algae, particularly the brown rather than the green, contain pigments differing slightly from those in higher plants. Instead of chlorophyll b a species of chlorophyll called chlorophyll c is abundant. It is suggested *Fucus* or *Laminaria* species be used. As is obvious from the colour of these algae, brown pigments will predominate over the green. β-carotene and various xanthophylls (for example, fucoxanthin, butein and violaxanthin) will be present in addition to chlorophylls a and c.

In exp. 46 the Hill reaction is performed by illuminating the reaction mixture for 15 seconds followed by a 'dark period' whilst a colorimeter reading is taken. This interruption to illumination may affect the reaction rate. Students might investigate this point by comparing reaction rates of mixtures that are subjected to constant and interrupted illumination for the same total time of light.

Heating to 50°C rapidly inactivates isolated chloroplasts. Students might attempt experiments to obtain a time course of inactivation of Hill reaction activity. It is suggested that very thin glass tubes are used with very small volumes of chloroplasts. This will aid heat transfer during heating to 50°C prior to assaying Hill reaction activity at room temperature. Inactivation is very rapid and students will find that 2 minutes at 50°C is usually enough to give complete inactivation.

7 Water and salt relations

7.1 Water relations

Water is an essential constituent of plant cells. It serves the special functions of maintaining plant shape and form and being the solvent for the entry and movement of soluble substances throughout the plant. Water is also required as the solvent for metabolic reactions and may itself be a reactant.

The plant cell wall, composed mainly of cellulose, is capable of being stretched to a certain extent. The wall is permeable to both water and solutions (except where it is thickened). Most of the cell volume is occupied by a vacuole which contains an aqueous solution of both organic and inorganic substances. The vacuole is separated from the cell wall by two membranes — the tonoplast and the plasmalemma — which themselves contain the cytoplasm.

Generally membranes are readily permeable to water but not to solutes; such a membrane is said to be 'semi-permeable'. The process by which water crosses such membranes is known as 'osmosis' and this may be defined as the movement of water from a weaker solution to a more concentrated solution when the two are separated by semi-permeable membrane.

In the thermodynamic terms water has a chemical potential and will move from a region of high chemical potential to one of lower chemical potential. The term 'water potential' is used to describe the energy status of water in a system. So in osmosis water flows in the energetically downhill direction — from higher to lower water potential. By convention the reference and maximum value for water potential is taken to be pure water at atmospheric pressure and is assigned a zero value. Any other solution will therefore have a lower (negative) water potential value.

Osmosis can be demonstrated using an osmometer (Fig. 13). Water will move from the beaker across the membrane into the sucrose solution. This movement may be opposed by applying pressure to the

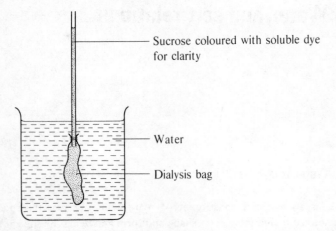

Sucrose coloured with soluble dye for clarity

Water

Dialysis bag

Fig. 13   A simple osmometer

solution and it is possible to measure the hydrostatic pressure required to stop the flow of water through the membrane. This pressure is the osmotic pressure of the solution and is proportional to the number of particles of solute in the solution, whether ions or molecules. Obviously a solution will not show a pressure unless placed in an osmometer and so the term 'osmotic potential' is used. The osmotic potential of a solution can be regarded as a measure of the tendency for water to flow into that solution. The presence of solute particles will lower the water potential of a solution since for a given volume a solution contains less water than the same volume of pure water. So the more concentrated a solution is, the less water it will contain and the greater its osmotic potential and the lower (more negative) its water potential.

Vacuolated plant cells behave as osmometers since the vacuolar solution is separated by semi-permeable membranes from the external solution. The dissolved substances in the vacuole result in water potential being low, so if the cell is placed in pure water (water potential maximum) then water will move down the gradient from higher to lower water potential and thus enter the cell vacuole. As this occurs so the contents of the vacuole are diluted and the vacuole will expand, forcing the cytoplasm against the cell wall. This force, turgour pressure, will cause an equal and opposite reaction and the wall pressure thus generated will tend to force water out of the cell vacuole. So the tendency for water to enter the cell will be governed by the water potential gradient between the cell and the external solution and by the extent to which wall pressure opposes vacuole expansion. Water will cease to be taken up by the cell when the force of the wall pressure is sufficient to counter-balance the force of vacuole expansion even though a water potential gradient still exists. At this point the cell is said to be turgid.

When a cell is placed in a concentrated solution (lower water potential than the vacuolar sap) then water will move down the gradient and leave the cell. As this occurs the contents of the vacuole are concentrated whilst turgour and wall pressure decrease. If water continues to leave the cell, i.e. a water potential gradient still exists, both turgour and wall pressure will eventually become zero. If the process continues the cell wall begins to distort and the cytoplasm will separate away from the wall. At this stage the cell is said to be at 'incipient plasmolysis' and as this process continues the cell will become 'plasmolysed'.

A solution in which a cell's volume decreases is said to be 'hypertonic' and a 'hypotonic' solution is one in which the cell volume will increase. A solution in which a cell's volume remains constant is said to be 'isotonic'.

Osmotic water uptake is the major method by which plants obtain their water, although there are many reports of non-osmotic water absorption by processes requiring the expenditure of metabolic energy. It appears unlikely however that metabolic water uptake occurs other than perhaps in some very specialised cells and tissues.

Experiments 48–53

48: To illustrate osmosis

In this experiment osmosis of water takes place through a dialysis membrane into sugar solutions of different concentrations. The rate of osmosis will be measured.

Materials: 1 dm^3 (1 l) of 1 mol dm^{-3} (1 M) sucrose solution
            14 mm or $\frac{18}{32}$ in. dialysis tubing
            Thread
            5 of 250 cm^3 beakers

Method: Dialysis bags are prepared by cutting 14 mm dialysis tubing into 20 cm lengths. Tie one end securely with thread.
       Fill each bag as follows:

1.   15 cm^3 of tap water

2.   15 cm^3 of 0.5 mol dm^{-3} (0.5 M) sucrose
3.   15 cm^3 of 0.75 mol dm^{-3} (0.75 M) sucrose
4.   15 cm^3 of 1 mol dm^{-3} (1 M) sucrose
5.   15 cm^3 of tap water

After filling each bag remove the air by carefully squeezing below to bring the liquid to the top of the bag. Press the sides of the bag together so that air does not re-enter. Fold the end of the bag over about 2 cm and tie securely with thread.

Weigh each bag separately to the nearest 0.1 g and record the masses at time zero. Place bags 1, 2, 3 and 4 in separate beakers of water and bag 5 in a beaker of 1 mol dm^{-3} sucrose solution.

At 15-minute intervals, up to a total of 75 minutes, remove the bags, carefully wipe off all excess water and weigh each bag.

Plot a graph of changes in mass of each bag against time. Plot another graph of the initial rate of water uptake (for bags 2, 3 and 4) against sucrose concentration.

Discussion: The bags 2, 3 and 4 gain mass. This is because the water potential of the sucrose solution inside the bag is lower than the water outside; consequently water will move into the bag. The dialysis tubing is acting as a semi-permeable membrane in that it allows movement of water but retains the sucrose. Bag 1 acts as a control to show osmosis only occurs where a gradient of water potential exists. Bag 5 shows again movement of water in response to a water potential gradient and that the membrane permits water movement in either direction.

The time courses for osmosis in bags 2, 3 and 4 tend to level off towards the end of the experiment. This is because the walls of the dialysis bags can only stretch to a limited extent and will then oppose further water entry. This is analagous to wall pressure of a cell opposing vacuole expansion.

The graph of rate of water movement shows the greater the concentration of sucrose solution (and hence the lower the water potential), the greater the rate of water movement since a large gradient of water potential exists.

49: To determine the mean osmotic potential of the contents of cell vacuoles in a tissue

This determination rests upon the assumption that when a cell is either plasmolysed or shows incipient plasmolysis the vacuolar osmotic potential (OP) equals the OP of the plasmolyticum. The method outlined here permits an estimation of the mean OP of the vacuolar contents of a tissue and not the OP of a specific cell.

Materials: 500 cm^3 of 0.6 mol dm^{-3} (0.6 M) sucrose
Two of the following tissues, beetroot, onion epidermis, *Spirogyra Rhoea discolor* epidermis, *Bryophyllum* epidermis
Stop-clocks
Microscopes
12 glass slides or cover slips
12 petri dishes (plastic or glass) or 50 x 25 mm specimen tubes

Method: Prepare a series of sucrose solutions 0.1 mol dm^{-3} to 0.6 mol dm^{-3} (0.1 M to 0.6 M) and place them in petri dishes or 50 x 25 mm specimen tubes.

Run two series of experiments using two of the tissues suggested above. Pieces of tissue are mounted in the solutions and after 20–30 minutes each in turn is removed and placed on a slide in a little of the plasmolyticum. The number of plasmolysed and unplasmolysed cells are counted, and then the slide should be moved and a different field counted until about 50 or more cells have been examined. Count the number of plasmolysed and unplasmolysed cells in the tissue in each plasmolyticum and then tabulate your results. Plot the percentage cells plasmolysed against the concentration of the plasmolyticum and determine the concentration at which 50% of the cells are plasmolysed.

Discussion: Calculate the OP of the cells by the following formula:

$$OP = \frac{CRT}{M_1}$$

in which OP = osmotic pressure (potential) in N m^{-2}

C = solute concentration in g m^{-3} causing 50% plasmolysis

R = proportionality constant = 8.314 J K^{-1} mol^{-1}

T = temperature in K

M_1 = molecular weight of solute in g mol^{-1}

Since solutions have a lower water potential value than pure water a negative sign is given to the calculated osmotic pressure (potential).

(Alternatively the OP may be calculated in atmospheres using the expression:

$$OP = \frac{22.4 \, M \, T}{273}$$

in which OP = osmotic pressure (potential) in atmospheres

M = molar concentration causing 50% plasmolysis

T = temperature in K

Again a negative sign is given to the calculated value since solutions have a lower water potential than pure water.)

For non-electrolytes, e.g. sucrose, these formulae may be applied directly. But since osmotic potential depends on the number of particles (ions or molecules) in solution, the above formula needs to be corrected for ionisation if an electrolyte is used as the plasmolyticum.

The formula will give an approximate value since experimentally determined values are much lower than the calculated values. This is due to association between solvent molecules, and to hydration of solutes.

The method determines the mean OP of the cells and assumes that at incipient plasmolysis the turgour pressure is zero.

50: To determine the water potential of storage tissue

The water potential of a cell is a measure of the tendency for water to enter the cell when it is placed in water. The determination rests upon the fact that if the tissue has a lower water potential than pure water, it will take up water when placed in pure water and hence will increase in weight and volume. On the other hand if the tissue is placed in a solution which has a lower water potential, then the tissue will lose water and hence decrease in mass and volume. By using a graded series of sucrose solutions the water potential of a tissue can be determined as equal to the OP of that sucrose solution which results in no increase or decrease in the mass or volume of the tissue.

Materials: 10 potatoes or beetroots (as large as possible)
Cork borers (size 2 or 3)
Boiling tubes
Paper tissues
Balances
Rulers

Knives
Stop-clocks
500 cm^3 of 1 mol dm^{-3} (1 M) sucrose

Method (a). Gravimetric determination: Cut 21 cylinders (6–7 cm long) of tissue using the cork borer. Lightly dry and weigh the cylinders in groups of three to the nearest 0.01 g. Incubate each group of three cylinders in boiling tubes with sucrose solutions covering the range 0.1 mol dm^{-3} to 0.7 mol dm^{-3} (0.1 M to 0.7 M) for 1 hour. After 1 hour remove the tissues, lightly dry and reweigh each group of three cylinders.

Method (b). Change in length determination: As for method (a), but record the lengths (in mm) of each group of tissue cylinders at the start and end of the incubation in sucrose.

Discussion: Plot a graph of loss or gain in mass (length) against sucrose concentration and determine the molarity of the sucrose solution in which the tissue shows no change in mass (length). Calculate the OP of this sucrose solution.

51: To determine the temperature coefficient (Q_{10}) of water uptake by potato tissue

Plants obtain their water by osmosis which involves no expenditure of metabolic energy. Consequently the Q_{10} value should be characteristic of passive or non-metabolic processes (see also Chapter 4).

Materials: 5 knives
5 potatoes (as large as possible)
Cork borers (size 12)
20 thin plastic needles
20 boiling tubes
Paper tissues
Water baths at 25°C and 35°C
Stop-clocks
1 dm^3 (1 l) of distilled water
Balances
1 dm^3 (1 l) of 0.4 mol dm^{-3} (0.4 M) sucrose

Method: A day before the experiment cut plugs of potato with the cork borer and slice the plugs into thin (2–3 mm) slices – do not use the skin. Incubate the slices in the sucrose solution.

At the start of the experiment remove 10 discs from the sucrose, blot quickly and weigh. Space the discs on to the thin needles and immerse the discs in distilled water in a boiling tube previously equilibrated to 25°C. Start a clock and repeat the procedure for an incubation at 35°C. At the end of 30 minutes remove the discs from the water, blot and weigh. Repeat for the other set of discs.

Discussion: If W_1g represent the mass of discs at time zero and W_2g at time 30 minutes, then $(W_2 - W_1)$g is the mass of water absorbed by mass W_1g of tissue at 25°C. Similarly $(W_4 - W_3)$g is the mass of water absorbed by mass W_3g of tissue for the second set of discs at 35°C. Hence Q_{10} is calculated:

$$Q_{10} = \frac{(W_4 - W_3)}{(W_2 - W_1)}$$

Values less than 2 are indicative of non-metabolic processes.

52: Studies on membrane permeability

To determine the permeability of onion bulb epidermis to the dyes listed below with their molecular masses.

Methyl red	269
Neutral red	289
Methylene blue	320
Orange G	452
Basic Fuchsin	571
Erythrosin	990

Materials: Dilute solutions of equimolar concentrations of the above dyes
250 cm^3 of potassium chloride solution 0.5 mol dm^{-3} (0.5 M)
Onion bulbs
Boiling tubes
Microscope
Glass slides + cover slips

Method: Preliminary experiments should be performed using varying dye concentrations as, if the dye is too concentrated, observation is rendered difficult.

Mount onion epidermal tissue in one of the above dye solutions and examine after 10, 20 and 30 minutes. Plasmolyse with the potassium chloride solution and re-examine; this is necessary in order to be certain whether or not the dye has accumulated in the vacuole or whether it has merely stained the cytoplasm and cell wall. Cells killed by the possible toxicity of the dye or cells killed accidentally in preparing the tissue will not plasmolyse.

Discussion: Compare the penetration of the dyes with the two physico—chemical properties:

1. Rate of diffusion.
2. Lipid solubility.

Diffusion rates are compared by placing a little dyed solution in a test tube containing a glass tube filled with gelatin gel and noting the distance which the diffusion front has travelled after 2-, 4- and 7-day intervals.

Lipid solubility is best examined by shaking about 1 cm^3 of the dye solution in water with 1 cm^3 of benzene or benzene solution of lecithin. Some dyes will be found to be soluble and others insoluble in the benzene solutions.

Results may be tabulated in the form suggested below:

(a)	(b)	(c)	(d)	(e)	(f)	(g)	(h)

Insert in column: (a) name of the tissue;
                  (b) dye;
                  (c) concentration percentage;
                  (d) colour of cell +++, ++, +, 0;
                  (e) colour of vacuole;
                  (f) colour of protoplast;
                  (g) distance diffused in gel column in mm;
                  (h) benzene solubility.

53: The effect of temperature on loss of permeability

Materials: Beetroot, cork borer and razor blades
Distilled water
Boiling tubes
Thermometer
500 cm^3 beakers or water baths
Bunsen burner + tripods

Method: Cut slices of beetroot from plugs obtained by using the cork borer. Thoroughly wash the beet slices for 10 minutes in several lots of distilled water and then transfer them to distilled water in a boiling tube in which the experiment will be conducted. Place the boiling tube in a 500 cm^3 beaker containing water or a water bath whose temperature is initially 20°C. Leave for 5 minutes. Raise the temperature by 5° and hold at the new temperature for 5 minutes. Continue raising the temperature by 5° until 35° has been reached. When the temperature at which pigment loss occurs has been roughly estimated, try to make a more accurate estimate of the critical temperature.

Discussion: It should be noted that some colour loss occurs throughout the experiment; as permeability increases the end point should be very noticeable. This is due to loss of membrane structure.

7.2 Movement of water in plants

Transpiration, the loss of water vapour from the surfaces of the plant by evaporation and diffusion through pores (stomata or lenticels), is chiefly responsible for the movement of water through a plant although it may be supplemented by capillarity and root pressure. Accurate measurement of transpiration is extremely difficult. In this section experiments are described which are popularly used to demonstrate this phenomenon and root pressure. It is stressed that they are quantitatively of little value. The authors are however of the opinion that they are worth including since they do demonstrate transpiration and offer the student an opportunity to criticise both the apparatus and the experiments themselves.

Experiments 54–57

54: To demonstrate root pressure

Materials: Potted plant with woody stem, e.g. *Salvia*, *Coleus*, geranium
              or tomato
              Rubber tubing
              Soft wire
              Capillary tubing

Retort stand and clamps
Corks bored to take capillary tubing
Suitable water-soluble dye, e.g. methylene blue or eosin
Razors or sharp knives

Method: Prior to the experiment, well water the soil in the pot. With a razor or sharp knife cut off the stem of the plant 2—5 cm above the level of the soil. Slip about 8 cm of rubber tubing over the stump of the stem, so that about 5 cm protrudes. Secure the rubber tube to the stem by means of soft wire. The rubber tube should now be filled with a weak solution of dye, e.g. 0.1% methylene blue. Obtain about 0.5—1 metre of capillary tubing of bore about 1—2 mm, slip it through a cork and clamp the cork to a retort stand. About 15 minutes after attaching the rubber tube to the stump the capillary tube is attached and secured by wire to the open end of the rubber tubing. This should force some of the dye solution into the capillary tube. Care must be taken not to introduce air bubbles into the capillary. After the vertical capillary tube is in place mark the level of the dye solution and record this as zero. At intervals of 10 minutes for 2 hours measure the liquid level, recording all higher levels as plus and all lower levels as minus.

Record your results and plot a graph of change in height of the column against time. What criticisms can be made of this experiment?

Discussion: After 2 hours root pressure will continue to force water into the tube but it is now opposed by the pressure of the water column so will slow. The soil must be well watered since entry depends on the root cells having a higher osmotic potential than the soil solution.

55: The use of the potometer to measure transpiration rates under different environmental conditions

Materials: Darwin's potometers (other versions are available)
Branch of soft-leaved plant
Vaseline
Razors or sharp knives
Eosin or other water-soluble dye
250 cm^3 beakers

Method: Take a 250 cm^3 beaker of water and cut a branch of convenient length from a tree. Immerse the cut end in water as quickly as

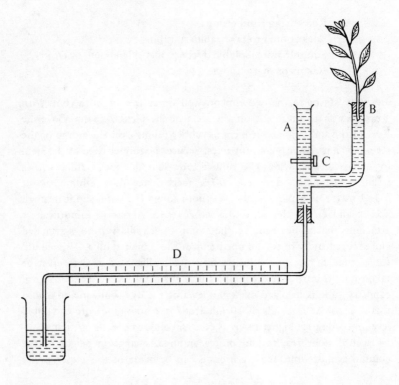

Fig. 14   Darwin's potometer

possible. In the laboratory, insert the end of the branch through the hole in the rubber stopper B provided with the apparatus. This should preferably be done under water. About 5–10 cm should protrude. Now remove 1–2 cm from the cut end. This should ensure that there are no air bubbles in the xylem.

By means of the reservoir A fill the apparatus with eosin-coloured water then close the tap C. Ensure that the well that is to take the plant is filled to the top and the capillary end is in a beaker of eosin solution. Quickly transfer the branch with the rubber stopper to the well and insert the stopper. There should be no trapped air bubbles beneath the stopper. Seal the stopper in position with Vaseline. The capillary end of the potometer should be lifted out of the beaker long enough for air to enter as the leaves transpire; re-immerse so that a bubble of air is caught. The bubble will travel along in front of the attached ruler D. When the bubble proceeds beyond the ruler it may be driven back by opening the tap C.

Discussion: The distance moved by the bubble per unit time is a measure of the rate of transpiration. The rate under different environmental conditions may be determined, e.g. in still air, in wind (in front of a fan), in the light and in the dark. For each condition continue measuring until three successive measurements have been obtained that show close agreement.

56: Transpiration from a detached leaf and linear rate of movement of water in the xylem

Materials: Convenient soft-leaved plant
Glass bulbs 2.5 cm diameter with a 2.5 cm stem
Specimen tubes
Hair-driers
Razor blades
Microscopes
Micrometer eye-pieces
Balances
Wax parafilm

Method: Remove a leaf from the plant by cutting through the petiole, leaving some petiole still attached to the stem. Immediately insert the petiole of the cut leaf into a glass bulb containing water and seal the top. Place the bulb and leaf in a specimen tube, and weigh (see Fig. 15).

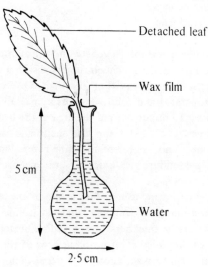

Fig. 15   Transpiration bulb for exp. 56

Remove the bulb and leaf from the tube and allow transpiration to proceed. Weigh as before every 15 minutes. When a steady rate is obtained try the effect of wind by using a fan or hair-drier.

While waiting to take readings use the petiole stump to make a transverse section of the petiole. With the help of a micrometer eye-piece and calibrated slide determine the total cross-sectioned area of the xylem in the petiole.

Discussion: Knowing the volume of water transpired per minute under particular conditions, you can now use the cross-sectioned area of the xylem to find the average rate of linear flow along the xylem elements. Thus rate of transpiration = x mm^3 min^{-1} and

$$\text{xylem area} = y \text{ mm}^2$$

$$\text{average rate of linear flow in xylem} = \frac{x}{y} \text{ mm min}^{-1}$$

57: Relationship of transpiration to leaf area and structure

Materials: *Heuchera* and laurel leaves
Wax parafilm
Small specimen tubes or glass bulbs
Balances
Nail varnish
Microscopes
Razor blades

Method: Remove a leaf of *Heuchera* and a leaf (or shoot) of laurel. Place the stalk or stem in a specimen tube of distilled water and seal the top around the stalk with wax film (see Fig. 15). Find the initial mass of the whole apparatus and follow the loss in mass due to transpiration by weighing every 15 minutes. Find the area of the leaves by tracing the outlines on paper, cutting out the leaf shape and weighing; compare with the mass of a known area of the same paper. Plot transpiration as mg water lost per minute per unit leaf area against time for the two species.

During the experiment, using other leaves of the same species make microscopic sections and compare their anatomies with particular regard to leaf cuticle thickness and the distribution of stomata. By using nail-varnish impressions of both surfaces of the leaves (paint the leaf surface with nail varnish, allow to dry and then peel off), compare the number of stomata per unit leaf area for both sides of the leaves.

Discussion: Cuticular transpiration is generally considered to be negligible except in very soft-leaved plants (e.g. *Coleus*). Stomata are the primary sites of water loss. Transpiration therefore may be commonly related to the number and size of stomata per unit area of leaf. Most plants possess stomata on their lower surface only, though a few possess them on both surfaces. In the latter cases there are generally fewer stomata on the upper surface.

7.3 Mineral nutrition of plants

Many elements are required by plants to a greater or lesser extent. They may be required for building essential chemicals or for the functioning of enzyme systems. Such irreplaceable elements are termed 'essential elements' (potassium, calcium, phosphorous, sulphur, magnesium, nitrogen). Other elements required in minute quantity are called 'trace elements' (iron, manganese, boron, copper, zinc, molybdenum, chlorine).

Deficiency diseases

In plants lacking an essential element, pathological symptoms develop. Retarded growth is a general symptom of deficiency but superimposed on this are usually more specific symptoms characteristic of the particular element that is lacking. Different kinds of plants do not all react similarly, or to the same degree, to deficiency of a particular element.

Deficiency of an element may be absolute or relative, i.e. it may arise directly from an acute shortage of the particular element in the soil (common in the case of nitrogen) or from a relative shortage induced or accentuated by an excess of some other element. Thus a deficiency of potassium may arise because of excess nitrogen or phosphorus. The pH (see Appendix 1) of the soil may also determine whether or not an element is readily 'available' to the plant. For example, iron and manganese are less readily utilised if the pH of the soil is high. Pathological effects may also occur if certain elements are too readily available. For example, in a calcium-deficient acid soil, the elements manganese and magnesium may be taken up in toxic amounts.

The following gives a general idea of the kind of symptoms usually observed when a particular mineral element is deficient.

Nitrogen. General stunting and sparcity of growth. Leaves generally pale and may assume bright yellow or reddish-purple tints. Blossoming, seed formation and fruiting are much reduced.

Phosphorus. Symptoms similar in many respects to those of nitrogen deficiency, but leaves darker green and often assume a purple or reddish colour. Brown spots may develop on the foliage.

Potassium. Growth stunted. Margins of leaves become yellowish and then brown and withered, the condition being referred to as 'marginal scorch'. Frequently seen in foliage of apple, pear, potato and other crop plants. Severe deficiency restricts growth of shoots and may cause them to 'die back'.

Calcium. Growth greatly retarded. Symptoms first appear near growing points and in roots. Leaves rudimentary, distorted, rolled and 'scorched'. Root systems poorly developed. In many species, the apical growing regions of shoots and roots rapidly disintegrate. Soil acidity, which accompanies calcium deficiency in the field, may induce manganese or magnesium toxicity symptoms as secondary effects.

Magnesium. Conspicuous yellow mottling of older leaves, the interveinal areas becoming yellow, mid-ribs and main veins remaining green. Leaves fall prematurely, often without previous withering.

Sulphur. Rarely seen. Younger leaves have pale green colour. Relatively little stunting.

Iron. Severe chlorosis (yellowing) of the apical leaves of young growths, generally followed by 'die back' of shoots. The leaves may be entirely bleached, or chlorosis may take the form of mottling, or interveinal yellow stripes.

Boron. Growing points of stems and roots of stems die, leaves show mottling and flower buds fail to develop. Fleshy tissues show internal browning and death of cells. Well-known examples are: 'Crown Rot' of sugar beet; 'Brown Heart' of turnips and swedes; 'Hollow Stem' or browning of cauliflowers.

Manganese. Frequently chlorosis, similar to that caused by iron deficiency (but not most severe in young leaves). Many plants show other characteristic symptoms. Examples: 'Grey Speck' of oats and 'Marsh Spot' of peas.

Copper. Marked yellowing and chlorosis of normally green tissue. Fruit trees very susceptible and show 'die back' of shoots.

Zinc. In herbaceous plants, yellowing of lower leaves at tips and margins. Necrotic patches on leaves and the latter often malformed. Serious effects on certain fruit trees which develop 'little leaf' disease.

Molybdenum. In cereals, brownish-red patches on upper leaves. Grain often fails to form.

Knowledge regarding the functions of the various essential mineral elements is incomplete. However, certain elements are obviously required because they are components of important cell substances. Many enzymes contain or require metals for activation.

Nitrogen. Component of proteins, nucleic acids, chlorophyll and other important organic compounds.

Phosphorus. Constituent of proteins, lecithins, nucleic acids and ATP.

Sulphur. Closely associated with nitrogen metabolism. Constituent of certain amino-acids and other important organic compounds. The sulphydryl (−SH) group is important in certain enzymes.

Magnesium. Constituent of chlorophyll and also necessary for esterification of phosphorus into ATP. Magnesium ions activate various enzymes.

Calcium. Required for uptake of nitrate ions, therefore is interrelated with nitrogen metabolism, a constituent of middle lamella. Increases elasticity of cell walls. 'Lime-induced chlorosis' depends on the ratio of calcium to potassium.

Potassium. Not known as a constituent of any organic compound. Associated with carbohydrate metabolism. Believed to play a fundamental role in the maintenance of protoplasmic organisation and permeability.

The small amounts of trace elements that are needed by plants suggest a catalytic function as components of prosthetic groups or activators of enzymes. Some of the functions of trace elements are as follows:

Iron. Involved in formation of chlorophyll and of chloroplastic protein. Component of prosthetic group of cytochromes, peroxidase and catalase. (If ratio of iron to phosphorus is outside a certain range, chlorosis results.)

Copper. Component of prosthetic group of polyphenol and ascorbic acid oxidases; it therefore has a possible role in respiration.

Manganese. Activator of certain enzymes. Believed to be related to oxidation-reduction reactions in which iron plays a part.

Zinc. Associated with formation of tryptophane, an intermediate in indole acetic acid synthesis.

Boron. In some unknown way affects water relations of plants, e.g. transpiration. Enhances translocation of sugars.

Chlorine. Activates certain enzymes.

Molybdenum. Essential for nitrogen fixation by bacteria and also for nitrate reduction (constituent of nitrate reductase and also of xanthine oxidase).

Experiments 58–59

58: To illustrate mineral deficiency symptoms in plants

Materials: Prepare the range of solutions indicated. The nutrient solution used in this experiment is based on those used at Long Ashton Research Station.

Solution	Strength
A. $Ca(NO_3)_2 4H_2O$ (M.W. 236)	7.9%
B. KNO_3 (M.W. 101)	3.4%
C. $NaNO_3$ (M.W. 85)	2.85%
D. K_2SO_4 (M.W. 174)	2.9%
E. $Na_2SO_4 \cdot 10H_2O$ (M.W. 322)	2.2%
F. $CaSO_4 \cdot 2H_2O$ (M.W. 172)	0.17%
G. $MgSO_4 \cdot 7H_2O$ (M.W. 247)	3.7%
H. $NaH_2PO_4 \cdot 2H_2O$ (M.W. 156)	2.1%
J. $Mg(NO_3)_2 \cdot 6H_2O$ (M.W. 256)	3.8%
K. Fe(II) (E.D.T.A.) or Na_2 E.D.T.A. 0.8 g and 3.0 cm^3 of 10% $FeCl_3 \longrightarrow$ 360 cm^3	
L. Micronutrient stock (see below)	
M. H_3BO_3	0.02%
N. Micronutrient-minus-Boron stock	

Micronutrient stock solution:

2.0 g $MnCl_2 \cdot 4H_2O \cdot$; 0.2 g $CuCl_2 \cdot 2H_2O$; 0.3 g $ZnCl_2$; 2.0 g H_3BO_3 and 0.05 g $Na_2MoO_4 \cdot$ in 1 dm^3 (1 litre).

(N.B. Sulphates may be more convenient than chlorides but it is not then possible to have sulphur deficient solutions.)

In making up such stock solutions 'Analar' grade reagents are used, when possible, with distilled water from Pyrex glass stills, or, alternatively, 'demineralised' water which has passed through 'mixed bed' ion exchange resins.

Method: Prepare the range of nutrient solutions shown in Table 7 from the stocks provided; quantities indicated are cm^3 of stock, which should then be made up to 500 cm^3.

Table 7

	A	B	C	D	E	F	G	H	J	K	L	M	N
1. Complete nutrients	5	5					5	5		5	0.5		
2. Phosphorus omitted	5	5			5		5			5	0.5		
3. Potassium omitted	5		5		5		5	5		5	0.5		
4. Calcium omitted		5	10				5	5		5	0.5		
5. Nitrogen omitted				5		15	5	5		5	0.5		
6. Magnesium omitted	5	5			10			5		5	0.5		
7. Sulphur omitted	5	5					5	5	5	5	0.5		
8. Iron omitted	5	5					5	5			0.5		
9. Boron omitted	5	5					5	5		5			0.5
10. (All micronutrients except B omitted)	5	5					5	5		5		0.5	

In addition to the above solutions a 'control', of distilled water only, should also be used. Young plants should be grown in these solutions. Use a representative of a dicotyledonous family and also a monocotyledonous representative. Observe at weekly intervals and record the symptoms observed.

59: Determination of potassium and/or chloride uptake

Materials: Carrots — several pounds of large ones
Cork borers (1 cm diameter)
Pestle and mortars
Filter funnels and papers
Flame photometer
Balance
Petri dishes and polythene grids to fit;
    200 cm^3 of 0.01 mol dm^{-3} (0.01 M) silver nitrate
    20 cm^3 of potassium chromate indicator
    250 cm^3 of 0.01 mol dm^{-3} (0.01 M) potassium chloride
    10 of 10 cm^3 burettes and stands

Method: About 200 slices of carrot cortical tissue (3 mm thick and 1 cm diameter) should be washed in distilled water for 48 hours prior to the start of the experiment.

Blot and weigh 10 discs and then boil them for a few minutes in 50 cm^3 of distilled water. Macerate the discs and dilute to 500 cm^3. Then filter a small quantity of the solution.

Determine the potassium ion concentration of an aliquot of the filtrate by means of the flame photometer and calculate the potassium ion concentration per gram of fresh mass of tissue.

Using another aliquot, determine the chloride ion concentration by titration with the silver nitrate using potassium chromate as indicator. Calculate the chloride ion concentration per gram of fresh mass of tissue. (1 cm^3 of 0.01 mol dm^{-3} silver nitrate $\equiv$ 0.35 mg chloride.)

Now blot and weigh 50 discs and place them on a polythene grid in a petri dish and fill the dish with the solution of potassium chloride until the discs are awash.

Incubate for 2–4 hours then blot and reweigh the discs. Boil the discs in 50 cm^3 of distilled water, macerate, dilute to 500 cm^3 and filter a small quantity of the solution. Determine the potassium and chloride ion concentrations as before. Tabulate your results as follows:

	Initial readings	2- to 4-hour readings
Fresh weight		
K$^+$ content		
K$^+$ content g^{-1}		
Cl$^-$ content		
Cl$^-$ content g^{-1}		

The amounts of potassium and chloride absorbed may then be found by subtraction of the initial content g^{-1} value from the final content g^{-1} value.

Projects

Experiment 52 investigates one aspect of membrane permeability, namely the rate of penetration related to molecular size. It indicates, however, that other factors, such as lipid solutibility, will affect penetration. Since membranes are composed of amphoteric molecules such as proteins and lipids it is therefore likely that factors such as ionic charge will also influence penetration. Lipids do not freely mix with charged molecules or ions. Penetration by ions may be studied by placing epidermal strips of onion in 1 mol dm^{-3} (1 M) solutions of various ions on a glass slide, covering with a cover slip and observing microscopically. Plasmolysis will occur, but if the ions penetrate the membrane the cells will recover from the plasmolysis. The rate of recovery is directly related to the speed of entry. Students might be encouraged to devise experiments using ionic solutions of their own choosing. They should be reminded, however, that organic charged molecules such as citrate or acetate will affect the lipid structure of the membrane.

Organic solvents such as chloroform may destroy the lipid component of the membrane with consequent loss of permeability. Using beetroot slices (see exp. 53), place discs in water saturated with chloroform and note the loss of the betacyanin from the tissue. Students might investigate the effects of other organic solvents.

The protein component of the membrane can be denatured using 1 mol dm^{-3} (1 M) sodium hydroxide or (1 M) hydrochloric acid, beet discs may be incubated with either and the effect on permeability noted. It should be noted however that betacyanin changes colour with pH.

Experiment 55 describes a method for measuring the transpiration rate of a cut shoot. Students may devise experiments determining the effects of varying environmental conditions on the rate of transpiration by the shoot. By using a fan with variable speed it should be possible to simulate wind conditions of different speeds. These may be compared to a control plant in still air. It would be expected that the rate of transpiration would increase with increasing wind velocity up to a maximum when no further increase would occur and transpiration might even decline. This is due to changes that occur in the stomata of a leaf. In still air, stomata are barely open; as wind velocity is increased they will open more, but then water loss from the leaf becomes high and the stomata close, lowering transpiration rates. Again this can be followed by using nail varnish impressions (see exp. 57).

Similarly temperature may affect transpiration by influencing evaporation rates and stomatal opening (remember too in soft-leaved plants cuticular transpiration occurs and may amount to 10% of the total water loss). Students may investigate the influence of temperature assuming suitable incubators are available. If incubators are not available, care must be taken in improvising, as using heaters near the plant will set up air currents and the moving air will influence the results. Placing plants in a sunny window might affect (it could be argued) the available carbohydrate which in turn might influence stomatal movement. Another factor which would influence transpiration therefore would be availability of carbohydrate. Generally plants close their stomata at night and open them in the day. This is, however a generalisation; stomata species vary and plants may close their stomata in the day depending on available water, wind velocity and many other factors.

Similar variations in exps. 56–58 may be considered if more convenient. Students might investigate the contributing influences of cotyledons, young foliage leaves and roots, to transpiration in seedlings. Sunflower seedlings are excellent material and students should remove the various organs singly from different seedlings.

Experiment 59 describes methods for determining salt uptake by tissue. Salt absorption in tissues has two components. There is a physical absorption which is reversible (i.e. the salt may be washed back out), is not selective between ions and which has a low Q_{10} in the region of 1.2—1.5. The other component, active absorption, is dependent on metabolic energy and therefore has a high Q_{10} (2—2.5), is selective, and is irreversible. This active absorption provides the larger component at reasonable temperatures. At low temperatures this component will be small. At 1°C therefore uptake will be due almost entirely to physical absorption. Dead tissues likewise will only be capable of physical absorption. Students might, if facilities permit, investigate the effect of temperature on uptake. Likewise, since active absorption depends on metabolic energy, respiratory inhibitors such as dinitrophenol (DNP) will prevent active absorption. A concentration of 10^{-4} mol dm^{-3} (10^{-4} M) will achieve effective inhibition.

Warning

If inhibitors are used great care must be taken. DNP will prevent ATP formation in man as in plants, it is easily absorbed through the skin and there is no way of preventing it from acting once it is absorbed. Should a student through accident get the solution on his skin, immediate scrubbing should be employed. Similarly other respiratory inhibitors such as cyanides and azides are highly toxic, and should NEVER be pipetted by mouth and should be handled with great care.

The uptake of ions other than potassium and chloride may be investigated, e.g. ammonium ion concentration may be estimated using Nessler's reagent (in this case it is interesting to monitor the pH of the medium at 30-minute intervals for 2—3 hours).

8 Growth and hormonal control

8.1 Growth

Growth is difficult to define although easy to recognise. An increase in the height or the girth of a plant represents growth as does the increase in volume of a developing fruit. The processes involved in such increases are complex but initially all involve cell division. There are, however, examples of growth in which cell division does not take part; pollen tubes grow down the style without cell division. This is an example of increase in cell length. It is possible then to consider growth as an increase in cell structural material usually involving cell division and enlargement. This manifests itself by increase in volume and mass of the tissue or organ of the plant.

Not all volume increase, however is due to growth. A flaccid leaf may increase in volume when water is absorbed but this does not represent growth. Growth must be an irreversible process. Similarly growth may take place with an overall decrease in dry mass. A seed germinated and growing in the dark may use its food reserves to build new cells in the root and shoot. New structural materials are being synthesised by transferring material from the cotyledons to the root and shoot, but no new materials are being made, since photosynthesis cannot take place. Due to respiration, there is, in fact, a loss in mass.

Growth can perhaps best be defined as an irreversible increase in cellular structural materials usually accompanied by increases in fresh and dry masses and often involving cell division.

As far as whole plants are concerned overall growth can be measured in a number of ways which may not accurately estimate total growth but will give a reliable indication of the overall growth at least for purposes of comparison. Measurement of the height of a shoot as an estimate of shoot growth does not take into account the development of leaves, buds or increase in girth but does allow a comparative estimate of the growth occurring within shoots. Similarly, measurement of the increase in length of the main root can allow comparison of growth rates of roots under different conditions but it ignores development of lateral roots.

Fresh or dry mass measurements can indicate the total amount of plant growth or total root or shoot growth but give no information as to how the growth was distributed. To record the different aspects of growth therefore several measurements must be made. It would be desirable to record shoot height, number of internodes, number of lateral branches, bud development, flower initiation, fresh mass and dry mass, root length, number of lateral roots, root fresh mass and dry mass. It must be apparent that such measurements, though recording some of the many facets of growth, would be laborious and time consuming. Overall growth is therefore often conveniently measured in terms of fresh and dry masses or shoot height and root length.

Experiments 60–74

60: A comparison of the growth of seedlings in light and dark

Materials: Peas, variety Alaska or Meteor (500 approx.)
Balance
Oven
Razor blades or cutting instruments
6 seed trays
Sand or vermiculite
Blotting paper
10 of 100 cm^3 flasks and stoppers

Method: Soak a large number of Alaska or Meteor peas for 24 hours. Remove 20 of the peas and blot dry. Place in a flask whose mass when stoppered is known. Find the mass of the flask and the peas and record the fresh mass of the 20 peas.

Remove the stopper and calculate the mean mass. Place the flask in an oven at 60°C for 48 hours then allow the flask to cool, stopper again and find its mass. Place the unstoppered flask back in the oven at 60°C for a further 6 hours then cool and find its mass again. The mass should be the same as after the 48-hour oven drying. If it is not, re-dry until a constant mass is obtained. Incomplete drying can introduce a large error into dry mass measurement. Calculate the mean mass per seed.

This should give a value for the initial fresh mass and dry mass of plants and the mean value for any one plant.

Divide the remainder of the soaked peas into six lots of twenty, and place each lot in six seed trays containing 5–6 cm of vermiculite or sand. Bury the seed about 10 mm below the surface. Place three of the trays in a dark cupboard at 20°C, or as near as possible to this temperature, and the other three trays in the light at the same temperature.

Water each tray regularly for the next 7 days. At the end of this time remove the seedlings carefully from one tray that has been in the light and one that has been in the dark. Wash the sand or vermiculite from the roots, blot dry and determine fresh mass as before.

Now measure the length of the shoot and the length of the main root of the 20 plants. Lastly obtain dry mass values as previously described. Repeat twice with one box from the light and one from the dark, i.e. approximately 20 plants of each after 14 days and 21 days.

Record your results as shown in Table 8

Table 8

		Day 0	Day 7	Day 14	Day 21
Mean fresh mass	Light				
	Dark				
Mean dry mass	Light				
	Dark				
Mean shoot length	Light	—			
	Dark	—			
Mean root length	Light	—			
	Dark	—			

Represent your results graphically and comment on the significance.

Discussion: Depending on the plant tissue the rate of oven drying can be speeded up or slowed down by varying the temperature. It is important to reduce charring of the sample since this will introduce error into dry mass measurements. The estimates of growth by the dry mass and length method should follow the same pattern. Variations in fresh mass may occur depending on frequency of watering and hence turgidity of the plant. This experiment, though very simple in outline, has the merit of providing the student with the opportunity of becoming aware of possible errors in experimentation of this kind, some of which are indicated here.

61: To determine the distribution of growth in roots

Materials: 6 in. of steel wire (should be bendable but not too soft)
Cotton
Indian ink
200 peas
Razor blades
50 cm^3 of 0.01−0.05% neutral red dye
Test tubes
Filter paper
Seed trays and vermiculite
Microscope

Method: Soak about 30 pea seeds for 24 hours, plant in seed trays containing vermiculite and allow them to germinate for 3−4 days.

Bend the steel wire in a U-shape that cotton may be tied across the two ends. This then can be used as a marking device. The cotton should be dipped into the Indian ink.

Select seedlings with a reasonably straight primary root which is at least 2 cm long. Lay the root alongside a rule and, with the cotton, mark the root at 2 mm intervals. Note the time.

Wedge the pea seed in the top of a test tube using damp cotton wool and with a small amount of water in the bottom of the test tube. Stand vertically and leave for 24 hours. Repeat with five more seedlings.

At the end of the 24 hours take two tubes and measure the distance between the Indian ink marks and plot a graph showing percentage elongation at different distances from the tip.

Cut longitudinal sections of the root and place them in 0.01−0.05% neutral red. This dye will indicate the regions where vacuoles are developing. Mark this region on the graph and also the region where root hairs develop.

Allow the other seedlings to continue growing for a further 24 hours and repeat the measurement of the distance between Indian ink marks.

Discussion: It should become apparent that the region of elongation is set back from the tip of the root, illustrating that though the cell division region may be at or near the tip this is not the region which contributes markedly to the longitudinal extension. The location of vacuoles indicates areas of differentiation where cell extension continues. This presupposes that meristematic cells do not possess vacuoles.

62: Effect of decapitation on the growth of pea roots

Materials: Seed trays with vermiculite
200 peas
Test tubes
Cotton wool or filter paper
Microscope
Rubber bands
Micrometer eye-piece

Method: Soak pea seeds for 24 hours and plant in vermiculite in seed trays. After 2 days remove a seedling and mount in a test tube using filter paper or cotton wool to wedge the pea in position. Place a small amount of water (1 cm^3) in the bottom of the tube. Place a microscope in the horizontal position and secure the test tube to the vertical stage by means of rubber bands. Keep the tube and root vertical. With the 16 mm ($\frac{2}{3}$ in.) objective measure the growth of the root with a micrometer eye-piece at 5- or 10-minute intervals. After 1 hour, remove the seedling from the tube and excise a 1 mm tip. Replace the root and continue the measurements for a further 1 or 2 hours. Plot growth against time and then plot growth rate against time.

Discussion: Growth should be very reduced, the meristematic region having been removed. Over a longer period of study the root should develop a 'physiological tip' and some recovery of growth should be attained. The value of experiments where severe damage is inflicted to the organ can be discussed.

8.2 Hormones in plants

Hormones in plants can be defined as chemical substances of biological origin, other than nutrients, which in small quantities promote, inhibit or in some other way modify a physiological process, remote from the site of production.

Within plants a number of hormones exist, associated with the many physiological processes. Many of these chemical hormones have been classified on the basis of either chemical structure or the effects they produce.

8.2.1. Auxins

An *auxin* is a hormone characterised by its ability to produce elongations in shoots and inhibit the elongation of roots. The most important of these auxins are the indole auxins. These all possess a basic indole ring in their structure but vary regarding the side chains on the ring. Indole-3-acetic acid (IAA) is one of the most important of these (see Appendix 6).

The quantities of the indole auxins within plants are very low. Even minute quantities, however, at concentrations of 10^{-10} mol dm^{-3} (10^{-10} M) or lower can produce marked physiological effects. One of the difficulties in working with such small quantities is that it often becomes difficult to devise methods sensitive enough to accurately record the amounts present. Any technique which relies on a chemical reaction will not be sufficiently sensitive at these low concentrations.

Since plant material is sensitive to these very low concentrations, techniques have been developed which use the response of plant material to estimate concentration. Such techniques are termed bioassays.

For indole auxin and particularly IAA, the wheat coleoptile test has proved the most popular and one of the most reliable.

Experiments 63–66

63: The effect of auxin on the growth of coleoptile

Materials: Seed boxes or trays
           Wheat grains
           Petri dishes (disposable, plastic are satisfactory)
           Measuring cylinders
           Pipettes
           500 cm^3 of 10 mg dm^{-3} aqueous solution of IAA (dissolve the IAA in 2 cm^3 of ethanol and add water to volume)

Method: The wheat grains used for this experiment should be preferably 'undressed seed', i.e. they should not have been treated with fungicide. Before growing the wheat for the experiment it is advisable to test grow a small sample to determine the rate of germination.

Soak the wheat seed in water for 4–5 hours before sowing. Sowing may be in sand or vermiculite. Place between 4–5 cm of sand or vermiculite in a tray and press down gently. Sow the seed liberally over the surface and cover with 1.0 cm of sand or a thin layer of vermiculite. Water, taking care not to expose the grain. Obtain as even a watering as possible but do not over-water. Store the trays at 25°C in an incubator. If an incubator is not available, place the tray in a cupboard or other light-proof container and keep in a temperature as near 25°C as possible. It is important that the temperature be kept as uniform as possible. Water the trays once a day. Take care not to leave the trays too long in the light during the watering period.

At 25°C the young shoots with their coleoptiles should attain a length of about 2 cm in about 72 hours. The lower the temperature the longer they will take to attain this length. The higher the temperature the shorter the incubation period.

It should be remembered that the coleoptiles grow quickly and an extra 12 hours in incubation can result in coleoptile lengths well in excess of that required and often with the young leaves protruding.

A 'trial run' under the conditions you can provide is thus advisable before class use. One tray about 22 x 15 cm will be necessary for each pair of students.

From the IAA solution at 10 mg dm^{-3} prepare dilutions at 1.0 mg dm^{-3}, 0.5 mg dm^{-3} and 0.1 mg dm^{-3}. Place 10 cm^3 of each of the four concentrations into separate petri dishes, and place 10 cm^3 of distilled water in a fifth dish. (N.B. This will ensure that each pair of pupils has a series of four dishes containing IAA solutions at 10, 1.0, 0.5 and 0.1 mg dm^{-3} and one dish with distilled water.) Remove groups of wheat seedlings from the trays by lifting from underneath the seeds. Do not handle the coleoptiles at this stage. Cut the coleoptiles at their attachment to the grain. Select 50 coleoptiles of *uniform length*, preferably about 2 cm. Lay each coleoptile on mm graph paper and decapitate each coleoptile by removing 2 mm of the tip with a sharp blade. Then, cut a portion 10 mm long. The coleoptiles should be handled gently. As the sections are being cut deposit them into a beaker of distilled water. When you have cut 50 sections, remove them from the water and place 10 in each petri dish so that they float. Shake the dishes gently. Store them covered in a warm place (25°C is adequate), for the next 20–24 hours. The time must be the same for all the dishes. After this time measure the sections to the nearest mm, again using graph paper. If they are curved you must straighten them before measuring. During the incubation period the leaf may have projected from one end of the coleoptile; care must be taken *not* to include the leaf in the measurement. Record the lengths of the segments and calculate the mean (average) length (Table 9).

Table 9

Concentration of IAA mg dm^{-3}	10·0	1·0	0·5	0·1	0
Mean length					

Plot a graph of percentage elongation against log concentration of IAA.

Using this graph it is now possible to determine the concentration of a solution of IAA, whose strength is not known. Into 10 cm^3 of the solution place 10 1 cm coleoptile sections as before and after the same interval of time (20—24 hours) measure the percentage elongation. Read off the graph.

Discussion: In any bioassay technique accuracy depends on familiarity with the technique and the standardisation of possible variable factors such as temperature. For the biossay to produce consistent results, therefore, repetition of the experiment is necessary. Class experiments performed for the first time should indicate in broad terms the type of response but different groups within a class may be expected to produce variable results.

64: The effect of auxin on the growth of cress roots

A second bioassay procedure for the indole auxins, which has been widely used, involves the growth response of roots to the hormone. Cress roots are a useful experimental material since they grow at a convenient rate and are small enough to allow many seeds to be sown in a limited space. In all bioassay tests individual plants may vary slightly in their response; it is essential therefore that for each concentration of hormone as many plants should be included as possible. The larger the number, the less the chance that there will be error due to individual response variations. A very large number of plants in each concentration would be unmanageable. The experimental time would be too long and the supply of hormone, especially if extracted from plant tissue, may be limited. A convenient number of plants per treatment concentration thus must be chosen. This figure is usually about 20.

In comparing the results of this bioassay with the coleoptile test, it must be remembered that the concentration of auxins which stimulates the growth of coleoptiles inhibits that of roots but, at very low concentration, a slight stimulation of growth may be detectable.

Materials: Cress seed
Petri dishes (disposable are satisfactory)
Filter papers or germination papers
Pipettes
Measuring cylinders
500 cm^3 of 1 mg dm^{-3} (1 mg/l) IAA solution

Method: A day (24 hours) before the bioassay experiment a large quantity of cress seed should be sown fairly thickly on wet filter paper in petri dishes. These should then be stored in a warm place (around 25°C) to ensure satisfactory root growth.

Make up a stock solution of IAA of concentration 1.0 mg dm^{-3}. From this prepare a range of dilutions. A suggested range would be 0.1; 0.01; 0.001; 0.0001 mg dm^{-3}.

Place a filter paper in each of eight petri dishes and add 5 cm^3 of one solution to each of two of the petri dishes, 5 cm^3 of the next solution into the next two dishes and so on to complete the eight dishes. Prepare two control dishes of distilled water. From the germinating cress seeds select 100 seeds with roots of uniform length and arrange 10 seeds per dish. If possible keep them more or less equidistant. Place the dishes in a dark cupboard for 24 hours. At the end of this time the mean root length may be measured for each concentration, or alternatively, remove the cress seedlings from the dark and keep in normal daylight for 7 days. At the end of this time measure the root length. In either case record your results for mean root length and plot a graph (Table 10) to show the root growth against the logarithm of the auxin concentration.

Table 10

Concentration of IAA mg dm^{-3}	0·1	0·01	0·001	0·0001	0
Mean length of 20 roots					

Prepare another graph including the results of the coleoptile test and cress root test. Express all results as percentage increase or decrease in growth over the controls. Plot these figures against the logarithm of the auxin concentration in the form shown in Table 11.

Table 11

Increase in growth %

20

15

10

5

Control

Decrease in growth %

5

10

15

20

Log auxin concentration

Discussion: Although auxins are characterised by their effect on growth, the influence they have on plant development is much more extensive. They are involved in controlling such processes as root initiation, the inhibition of lateral buds by the terminal bud, leaf abscission, tropisms. In conjunction with other plant hormones they control other processes such as cambial activity.

65: The effect of auxin on apical dominance in bean plants

Materials: Seed boxes or trays

Dwarf or runner bean seeds (nine plants will finally be required per student)

100 cm^3 of lanolin paste

200 cm^3 of 1 g of IAA in a litre of lanolin paste

Prepare the paste by dissolving the required amount of crystalline hormone in a little absolute ethanol. Add this to the appropriate quantity of warmed hydrous lanolin. Stir vigorously to ensure a uniform mixture.

Method: Soak the dwarf or runner bean seeds in water for 24 hours and plant in soil. Grow in the seed boxes until the first trifoliate leaf has almost completely expanded and the first internode is fully extended. Remove the main shoot apex from six of the seedlings by cutting the tip off at the base of the first leaf. This should leave the first internode as long as possible. To the cut apex of three of the seedlings, apply sufficient of the IAA in lanolin paste to cover the cut end liberally. Cover the cut end of the other three seedlings with plain lanolin paste. Leave three other seedlings intact as controls. Measure the growth of the axillary buds of each series daily. Compare the results of the three series.

Discussion: The IAA should inhibit the development of axillary buds. Plants with lanolin alone should show bud development. In these plants one of the new growing buds will in turn show dominance. This may be observed by keeping the plant for several weeks. It should be noted that the implication here is that the apical bud produces IAA or an equivalent auxin and that this suppresses lateral buds as it is transported down the stem. It is just as likely, however, that the control on the development of axillary buds is due to more than one hormone and that the balance between them determines whether or not the bud develops. Removal of the terminal bud (the source of IAA) would upset that balance.

66: Effect of auxin on leaf abscission

Materials: *Method (a)*
5 coleus plants
500 cm³ of 3% agar
Razor blades
Petri dishes (30)
200 cm³ of 1 g IAA in 1 dm³
   of lanolin
200 cm³ of 5 g IAA in 1 dm³
   of lanolin
200 cm³ of 10 g IAA in 1 dm³
   of lanolin
Plain lanolin

Method (b)
5 coleus plants
Razor blades
Petri dishes (30)
Filter paper
Filter paper impregnated
   with 1 g dm⁻³ IAA

Method (a):   Make up a 3% agar solution, if possible under sterile conditions. Pour into large petri dishes to a depth of about 0.5 cm. Replace the lids immediately. Allow the agar to cool and solidify. Cut out an area of agar about 2 cm wide along the diameter of the dish as shown in Fig. 16.

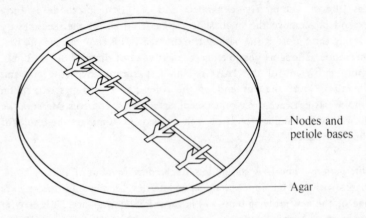

Nodes and petiole bases

Agar

Fig. 16   Arrangement of explants for exp. 66

Take a coleus plant and select pairs of opposite leaves from the 4th–8th node from the terminal unfolding leaves. Cut the stem about 0.25 cm above the node selected and 2.0 cm below. Trim off the leaf blades so that the petiole left attached to the stem is about 1 cm long. Apply to the cut end of both petioles enough of the 1 g IAA in lanolin to cover the cut surface. To similar explants apply plain lanolin, and one of the other two IAA in lanolin pastes. Use a minimum of five petiole pairs per treatment and apply, as near as possible, the same amount of paste.

Place in the petri dishes with the petioles overhanging the space and the stems resting on the agar as shown in Fig. 16.

Place the dishes in darkness. Examine daily by gently touching the petioles to determine whether abscission is ready to occur. Plot percentage petiole drop against days after treatment, for each treatment.

Method (b):   Cut out a node of coleus as in method (a), making the cut 1 cm above and 1 cm below the node. Remove the lamina as in method 1 and the axillary buds. Cut back the petiole to 1 mm from the stem. Split the stem vertically (see Fig. 17). Lay the cut stem surface downwards in a petri dish on moist filter paper or agar. Discs of filter paper should be impregnated with known doses of auxin solution

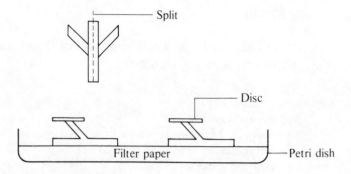

Fig. 17   Arrangement of coleus nodes for exp. 66

$(1 \text{ g dm}^{-3}$ to $10 \text{ g dm}^{-3})$ and, while the paper is still moist, place the discs on the cut surface of the petiole. As before, keep the sections in darkness at 25°C and record the 'abscission' of the different petioles every day.

Discussion: The delay in abscission caused by IAA may be interpreted as indicating a control mechanism whereby IAA is produced by the lamina during the growing season, but at the end of the season IAA levels fall, thus allowing abscission. Another interpretation might be that there is a balance between IAA and another hormone. For abscission to occur, the level of this other hormone must rise *and* IAA fall. This might explain why IAA can only delay abscission and not prevent it.

8.2.2. Gibberellins

A second group of plant hormones were discovered by the Japanese. These hormones were isolated from a fungus, *Gibberella fujikuroi*, which infects rice plants.

The infected rice plants showed a number of abnormal features. These effects were shown to be produced by hormones produced by the fungus. The hormones were termed gibberellins. Each of the gibberellins is abbreviated as GA and numbered GA_1, GA_2, GA_3, etc. The number of known gibberellins is increasing rapidly. In all extracts the predominant gibberellin is GA_3, known as gibberellic acid. All gibberellins have the same basic structure (see Appendix 6).

As with the indole auxins, estimation of low concentrations of these hormones is best carried out by a bioassay procedure.

Experiments 67–70

67: The effect of gibberellic acid on the growth of dwarf pea plants (*Pisum sativum* var. Meteor)

Materials: Seed boxes or trays
500 Meteor pea seeds
200 match sticks or small wooden pegs (mark with colour code for each concentration of GA_3)
0.01 cm^3 micropipettes
50 cm^3 of 1 g dm^{-3} (1 g/l) gibberellic acid solution. Prepare by dissolving in the minimum of ethanol and making up with water. Dilutions should be made so that in 0.01 cm^3 the mass is 10, 2.5, 0.5, 0.1, 0.05, 0.01 μg. The same amount of ethanol in the same volume of water should be made up for the control

Method: Soak and plant Meteor pea seeds in seed trays and grow until they are about 50 mm tall. Some 20–30 plants should be planted per tray and a total of six trays will be required.

When the plants are about 50 mm tall, measure the total height from soil level of all the seedlings in every box. Select half the seedlings at random for treatment and use match sticks or pegs to mark these.

Place one drop of an alcoholic solution of gibberellic acid on the centre of the leaflet of the first true leaf of each seedling – using the micro-pipette. These pipettes should be held vertical while the drop is applied so that the 'micro drops' are of exactly the same volume (0.01 cm^3).

Repeat in the other boxes so that each group of 10 plants has received doses of either 10 μg, 2.5 μg, 0.5 μg, 0.1 μg, 0.05 μg or 0.01 μg per plant.

The seedlings which have not been treated with gibberellic acid are the 'controls' and should have one drop of the alcohol water solution applied to the same leaflet as received the gibberellic acid on the treated plants. This is necessary in case the solvent affects growth.

Each box should be clearly labelled. The height of the seedlings and length of the internodes should be measured after 1, 2, 3 and 4 weeks from the start of the experiment.

Plot the increase in length of gibberellic acid treated seedlings over 'solvent only' treated seedlings against log concentration of gibberellic acid after 1, 2, 3 and 4 weeks (four curves).

Discussion: Note the effect of GA_3 at the end of the first week. Relate the effect produced to concentration. At the end of 3 weeks, the concentration which produces the maximum total growth has changed. Particular attention should be paid to the symptoms shown by plants treated with the higher concentrations, e.g. stem collapse leading to wilting unless the stem has been carefully supported.

A secondary bioassay technique for gibberellic acid is the lettuce hypocotyl test.

68: The effect of gibberellic acid on lettuce hypocotyls

Materials: Petri dishes
Lettuce seeds
Pipettes
Measuring cylinders
250 cm^3 of 100 mg dm^{-3} (100 mg/l) gibberellic acid solution

Germination of lettuce seed

Sow the lettuce seeds on moist filter paper in petri dishes and keep at 25° in the light. When the radicles of the seeds are approximately 5—6 mm long they are ready for use. It is as well to sow a number well in excess of the number required since you will need to select for uniformity. Do not use either those whose radicles are well in excess of 5—6 mm or those whose growth is slower.

Method: A stock solution of 100 mg dm^{-3} gibberellic acid should be prepared. Make a series of dilutions to give a range of concentrations of 10 mg dm^{-3}, 1.0 mg dm^{-3}, 0.1 mg dm^{-3} and 0.01 mg dm^{-3}.

Place a piece of filter paper in each of the six petri dishes. Pipette 5 cm^3 of each of the gibberellic acid solutions, one sample into each of five of the dishes. Into the sixth, pipette 5 cm^3 of distilled water. In each dish place 20 germinating lettuce seedlings with radicles 5 mm long. Leave the dishes in diffuse light for a period of 4—5 days. At the end of this time measure the lengths of the hypocotyls. During the 4—5 days the solutions may lose water by evaporation; this should be compensated for.

A preliminary run with water in a petri dish containing a filter paper will allow a fairly close estimate of evaporation rates.

Plot a graph of hypocotyl growth against the logarithm of gibberellic acid concentration.

Experiments illustrating the combined effects of indole auxins and gibberellins.

69: The effects of auxin and gibberellic acid on cambial activity

Materials: 50 poplar twigs
Beakers
200 cm^3 of 500 mg dm^{-3} (500 mg/1) IAA in lanolin
200 cm^3 of 500 mg dm^{-3} (500 mg/l) GA$_3$ in lanolin
200 cm^3 of an IAA/GA$_3$ mixture in lanolin, both at 500 mg dm^{-3}
The twigs needed for this experiment must be non-dormant and the experiment should be carried out before the buds open. In England this should be January–March. The twigs should be 0.7–1.0 cm in diameter

Method: The twigs should now be cut into 12–15 cm lengths (excluding the thinner apical regions). All lateral buds must be removed. The twig pieces must now be stood in water in a beaker. The lanolin paste should be applied generously to the upper cut end of each twig.

There should be at least four twigs, one with 500 mg dm^{-3} IAA in lanolin, one with 500 mg dm^{-3} GA$_3$ lanolin, one with a mixture containing 500 mg dm^{-3} of each in lanolin and one with plain hydrous lanolin.

Every 3–4 days make fresh applications scraping the surface or removing a very thin section below the old application. This will prevent any callous formation.

After a period of 3–4 weeks cut transverse sections of the stem at distances of 1 and 3 cm from the treated end and examine under the microscope. Stain your section with a xylem stain such as phloroglucin in concentrated hydrochloric acid. Draw regions around the cambium. Pay particular attention to the staining of the xylem near the cambium and to cell structure in the xylem.

Discussion: Though some cambial activity may be induced by IAA alone the xylem formed is abnormal and lacks lignin. Combinations of hormones produce more normal xylem. A combination of IAA/GA/cytokinin is preferable.

70: The effects of auxin and gibberellic acid on the rooting of cuttings

Materials: Dwarf bean seeds (about 300)
Seed boxes
Flower pots with sand for growing cuttings
750 cm^3 of 20 mg dm^{-3} (20 mg/l) GA$_3$
750 cm^3 of 200 mg dm^{-3} (200 mg/l) IAA
Solutions of GA$_3$ + IAA as indicated in method below

Method: Sow the soaked dwarf bean seeds in seed boxes so that you will have ultimately 150 plants. Grow the plants until the first trifoliate leaf is expanding. Cut off the seedlings at soil level. Disbud 60 cuttings and keep 90 with buds intact.

Divide the intact cuttings into groups of 10. Measure the lengths and then immerse the lower 3 cm of each group of 10 into one of the following aqueous solutions for 24 hours.

(*a*) Distilled water
(*b*) 1 mg dm^{-3} GA$_3$
(*c*) 10 mg dm^{-3} GA$_3$
(*d*) 50 mg dm^{-3} IAA
(*e*) 100 mg dm^{-3} IAA
(*f*) 2 mg dm^{-3} GA$_3$ + 100 mg dm^{-3} IAA 50 : 50
(*g*) 2 mg dm^{-3} GA$_3$ + 200 mg dm^{-3} IAA 50 : 50
(*h*) 20 mg dm^{-3} GA$_3$ + 100 mg dm^{-3} IAA 50 : 50
(*i*) 20 mg dm^{-3} GA$_3$ + 200 mg dm^{-3} IAA 50 : 50

After 24 hours remove the cuttings, shake off the excess solution and plant into the pots of sand. Leave in a light humid place, a greenhouse if possible, for 10–14 days.

Take the disbudded cuttings and again divide into groups of 10. During the course of the experiment new auxillary buds may develop. These must also be removed since they will synthesise auxin.

Measure the initial lengths of the cuttings (*after* disbudding) and then immerse the lower 3 cm of each group of 10 into one of the following aqueous solutions for 24 hours.

(*a*) Distilled water
(*b*) 1 mg dm^{-3} GA$_3$
(*c*) 10 mg dm^{-3} GA$_3$
(*d*) 50 mg dm^{-3} IAA
(*e*) 2 mg dm^{-3} GA$_3$ + 100 mg dm^{-3} IAA 50 : 50
(*f*) 20 mg dm^{-3} GA$_3$ + 100 mg dm^{-3} IAA 50 : 50

After 24 hours remove, shake off moisture and plant in sand in pots. Keep in a warm humid light place for 10—14 days.

At the end of the experiment measure the final mean length of the cuttings and record the number of roots per cutting in each treatment. Present your data as shown in Table 12.

Table 12

Concentration	Intact		Disbudded	
	Length of cuttings	No. of cuttings	Length of cuttings	No. of cuttings
1 mg dm^{-3} GA$_3$				
10 mg dm^{-3} GA$_3$				
50 mg dm^{-3} IAA				
100 mg dm^{-3} IAA				
2 mg dm^{-3} GA$_3$ + 100 mg dm^{-3} IAA				
2 mg dm^{-3} GA$_3$ + 200 mg dm^{-3} IAA				
20 mg dm^{-3} GA$_3$ + 100 mg dm^{-3} IAA				
20 mg dm^{-3} GA$_3$ + 200 mg dm^{-3} IAA				

Plot two graphs, one for intact and the other for disbudded cuttings, to show the relationship between root number per cutting and the mean increase in length of cuttings.

Discussion: The cuttings must be watered regularly after potting. They are very sensitive to water loss at this stage. Regular, light watering in a humid atmosphere, if possible, should be employed.

8.2.3. Cytokinins

In recent years a new group of plant growth hormones known as the cytokinins have been added to the auxins and gibberellins as key hormones in higher plants. The discovery of cytokinins was a direct outcome of research by Professor Skoog at Wisconsin University, USA. The compound he obtained was isolated from nucleic acid preparations and termed kinetin (see Appendix 6). To define a cytokinin is rather difficult. Skoog states that 'cytokinins are chemicals which, regardless of their other activities, promote cytokinesis in cells of various plant origins'. Perhaps not a very satisfactory definition, but since only one has been isolated a clear definition is difficult. Certainly all that can be said regarding their structure is that 'cytokinins are substances composed of one hydrophillic group of high specificity (adenine) and one lipophilic group without specificity'.

Most of the experimentation with this class of compound has been undertaken using Skoog's original kinetin. This and other cytokinin-like compounds have been shown to have diverse effects, from promoting cell division, to assisting in breaking seed dormancy.

Experiments 71–73

71: Radish leaf bioassay for cytokinins

Materials: Radish seedlings (dark grown, 3 weeks)
Petri dishes
500 cm^3 of $10^{-5} \text{ mol dm}^{-3}$ (10^{-5} M) kinetin
Micrometer eye-pieces
Microscopes
Balances

Method: Cut discs of about a half-inch diameter (a cork borer may be used) from leaves of radish seedlings grown in the dark. Float the discs on 7 cm^3 of kinetin solution in a petri dish. Use five discs in each. Weigh several sets of five discs at the start so that you can calculate an average mass at the beginning of the experiment. Kinetin will cause enlargement of the disc. Leave the discs in the dark in the kinetin for 7 days. Remove the discs, blot dry and re-weigh. Plot a graph of increase in size (mass) against kinetin concentration. It is suggested you use a range of concentrations in the range limits of $10^{-5} \text{ mol dm}^{-3} - 10^{-9} \text{ mol dm}^{-3}$.

A further exercise may be undertaken in this experiment. If at the beginning of the experiment some discs are examined under the microscope using a micrometer eye-piece calibrated with a stage graticule, the average cell length and number of cells along the diameter of the disc may be calculated. Repeat using the discs at the end of 7 days' treatment.

Discussion: It should now be possible to determine whether the effect is on cell division or enlargement or both. Whatever the conclusions drawn it must be remembered that it is dangerous to conclude that all kinetin effects on growth are due to this effect.

72: Effect of cytokinins on the expansion of discs of etiolated bean leaves

Materials: Bean seeds
Seed boxes
5 mm cork borer
Petri dishes
9 cm diameter filter paper
200 cm^3 of 3 μg dm^{-3} kinetin solution in 3% glucose by weight and 0.08 mol dm^{-3} (0.08 M) potassium nitrate, pH adjusted to 5.6
Green filters (Cellophane)

Method: Soak dwarf bean seeds for 24 hours and sow in sand at 25°C for 7–9 days in a dark cupboard. At the end of this period the plants should have produced the primary leaves just above the cotyledons.

Dilute the stock solution to give a range of concentrations 1.0, 0.3, 0.1 μg dm^{-3} in addition to the stock concentration.

Into each of four petri dishes put 5 cm^3 of solution, one sample of each concentration, and 5 cm^3 of water into the fifth dish. Put a disc of filter paper into each.

Remove the trays from the cupboard or dark storage space only after darkening the room. Place green filters over a convenient bench light source, so that all manipulations will be in dim green light.

Remove the primary yellow leaves and with a cork borer cut out discs of leaf 5 mm in diameter. Place in the five dishes, lower surface uppermost 10 discs per dish. Store in the dark at 25°C for 48 hours. At the end of this period measure the diameter of the disc at right angles to the main vein.

Record the increase in growth over the control and plot a graph of percentage increase over the control against concentration of kinetin.

73: Effect of kinetin on lettuce germination

Materials: Lettuce seed var. Grand Rapids
Petri dishes
9 cm filter papers
200 cm^3 of 20 mg dm^{-3} kinetin solution

Method: Place lettuce seed in petri dishes containing filter paper. Wet the paper with either 5 cm^3 of distilled water or 5 cm^3 of kinetin solution at concentrations 20 mg dm^{-3}, 10 mg dm^{-3}, 5 mg dm^{-3} and 2 mg dm^{-3}. Keep the dishes in darkness for 72 hours at 25°C or as near as possible to this temperature. Prepare a similar series of five dishes containing lettuce seeds and keep in darkness. Sixteen hours after placing this series in darkness, remove and expose to daylight for 8–10 minutes. Replace in darkness for 55 hours 50 minutes so that the total time from the start of the experiment is also 72 hours. Record the percentage germination in dishes in each series. In addition make observations on the root growth of the lettuce seedlings.

Table 13

Concentration of kinetin	Light treatment	Germination percentage
	Light (L)	
	No light (NL)	
20 mg dm^{-3}	L	
	NL	
10 mg dm^{-3}	L	
	NL	
5 mg dm^{-3}	L	
	NL	
2 mg dm^{-3}	L	
	NL	

Discussion: The lettuce seed variety used is important. Some varieties require light for germination and some not. Again this response to light may vary depending on temperature and age of the seed. There are too many commercially available varieties to list here but if Grand Rapids is not available preliminary experiments to determine seed behaviour with the varieties available will be necessary.

8.2.4. Abscisic acid

Studies on germination, dormancy and abscission during the 1950s revealed the presence of a widely distributed inhibitory compound. This was finally isolated and the structure-determined by Addicott. The structure of this compound is 3-methyl-5-(1'-hydroxy-4'-oxo-2',6',6'-trimethyl-2'-cyclohexen-1'-yl)-*cis,trans*-2,4-pentadienoic acid (see Appendix 6).

The trivial name of abscisin II was adopted for this compound and later (1966) it was renamed abscisic acid.

Abscisic acid has been identified in more than 30 species from ferns, grasses, beans, potatoes, apple, peach, etc., and in a range of organs from seeds, buds, stems, tubers, fruits, rhizomes.

This compound, and perhaps naturally occurring related compounds, interacts in nature with other growth-regulating chemicals and may be involved in processes such as transpiration, abscission, fruits, dormancy and, from evidence obtained of its interaction with other hormones, a number of other physiological processes. In its interaction with other hormones it may act antagonistically, or even synergistically depending on concentrations and the processes under examination.

It is possible that this and related compounds may be shown to be as important, in due course, as the gibberellins.

Experiment 74

74: Wheat embryo bioassay for abscisic acid

Materials: Wheat seed
Petri dishes
50 cm^3 of 250 mg dm^{-3} abscisic acid
Photographic enlarger
Filter papers

Method: Prepare a range of abscisic acid concentrations from 250 mg dm^{-3} to 0.2 μg dm^{-3}. Place 10 cm^3 of a particular concentration in a petri dish containing a filter paper. Repeat in other dishes with 10 cm^3 of the other concentration. On a moistened filter paper, place 10 embryos excised from dry wheat seed (these should be intact and as free as possible from adhering endosperm). Allow the embryos to grow for 2 days. Measure the embryos. To do this it will be easier to place them on a slide in a photographic enlarger and draw around the 'image'. Plot size (expressed as magnified units) against abscisic acid concentration.

Discussion: If it is not convenient to measure after 2 days the embryos may be stored in a refrigerator until convenient.

Projects

Allow students to grow wheat seed, and by sampling on a random basis measure growth at intervals. Students should be encouraged to determine for themselves the number of plants used in samples, the method of sampling and methods for measuring growth. The methods for measuring may be on the basis of fresh mass, dry mass, height of sward, leaf area or by any methods they can devise. They must include at least three methods and can then compare the results obtained for each method. As a supplementary, or alternative, exercise they might try to use the methods they employ to compare growth of plants which have developed in a mineral-deficient medium (see exp. 58).

Utilising the technique described in exp. 63, the following project might be suggested: In exp. 63 coleoptiles are grown by germinating wheat for 76 hours until the coleoptiles are approximately 2 cm tall. For the experiment, coleoptiles are selected and removed. The top 2 mm is discarded and the next 1 cm is used. Provided therefore the coleoptile is more than 12 mm tall and yet has not ruptured, it is considered usable. No account is taken of the variations in height of these coleoptiles prior to the experiment. It might be suggested to students that they investigate whether or not the initial height of the coleoptile has an effect on the subsequent response of the section to indole acetic acid. Students should, after planning their experiment, be reminded that an effect at one concentration of IAA does not mean necessarily that this effect is repeated to the same extent, if at all, at another.

Experiment 65 investigates the effect of auxin on apical dominance in plants. Students might like to investigate the effects of combining two or more hormones in the paste. It is suggested that they particularly consider combining indole acetic acid and kinetin. Suggested ratios of IAA to kinetin are 1 : 0.03, 0.02 : 2 and 0.2 : 2.

Germination of light-requiring lettuce seed can be achieved in darkness to a greater or lesser extent using hormones (exp. 73). Students could be asked to determine the effect of temperature on the response of a light-requiring variety to either gibberellic acid or kinetin or both, in darkness. They should record the percentage germination. Experimental design on the students' part will need to pay attention to adequate controls and relative as well as absolute concentrations of hormones (where two are used together).

Abscisic acid has been shown to be significant in the process of fruit abscission but less conclusively for leaf abscission. Using the explant technique illustrated in exp. 66 and with some idea of effective concentrations of abscisic acid from exp. 74, students might compare the effects of abscisic acid and indole auxins on leaf abscission. They might also try combining the two, again paying attention to relative as well as absolute concentrations.

9 Development of plants

9.1 Effects of light on plant growth and development

Light is essential for the life of a plant. The primary role of light in a plants existence is undoubtedly in photosynthesis.

However, light also influences many other processes directly. Etiolation, a phenomenon associated with growing plants in the dark and resulting in elongated yellow shoots, is suppressed by light. Light also determines the direction of growth of shoots (phototropism).

Seeds of some plants require light to germinate. Flowering in plants is often governed by the duration and intensity of daylight (photoperiodism). The following experiments illustrate a few of the effects of light on plant growth.

Experiments 75–78

75: To illustrate the effects of light in suppressing etiolation

Materials: Dwarf pea seeds, e.g. Meteor variety
Seed trays
Sand or vermiculite

Method: Soak the pea seeds for 24 hours and sow in sand or vermiculite in trays. Cover the seeds with the sand and place in a dark place, taking care to exclude light. Observations to determine germination should be brief and carried out in conditions of low light intensity.

When the seedlings emerge above the soil, subject them to a single light exposure varying in duration from 5 minutes to 4 hours. Keep one tray in continuous darkness. Replace the trays in the dark and observe the effects of light on the seedling development after a further 72 hours. Record the light effects on (*a*) chlorophyll development, (*b*) the expansion of the leaves, (*c*) the length of the internodes. With the tray in continuous darkness observe after 72 hours and note whether or not the terminal hook has uncurled.

Discussion: Etiolation or the lack of it, as with the uncurling of the terminal hook, is phytochrome mediated. Etiolation may be prevented by red light or normal daylight and the effect of light may be reversed using far-red light. Since the far-red-absorbing form of phytochrome can also revert to the red-absorbing form in darkness, darkness of far-red light may be used to induce etiolation. The uncurling of the terminal hook is also promoted by red light and prevented by far-red light or darkness.

76: To demonstrate the phototropic responses in oat coleoptiles

Materials: Oat grains
7.5 cm pots
Box 30 x 25 x 50 cm with an aperture 5 x 5 cm at one end
and a door at the other end
Razor blades
Aluminium foil
Match sticks
500 mg dm^{-3} IAA in lanolin paste (see exp. 65)
Lanolin paste

The box should be constructed to the dimensions indicated. Thin plywood is sufficient. To prevent light reflection the inside should be painted with a matt black paint (blackboard paint). The aperture should be centrally located on one of the 25 x 30 cm sides and can be made hinged or sliding. All joins should be light-proof.

Method: Sow the oat grains in 7.5 cm pots containing sand, soil or vermiculite. Water and keep in a warm place in complete darkness. When the oat seedlings have germinated and the coleoptiles are about 2 cm (normally 3 days at 25°C or longer at lower temperatures, sooner at higher), apply the following treatments using at least two coleoptiles for each.

(*a*) Leave the coleoptiles intact.
(*b*) Remove the top 2 mm of the coleoptile with a sharp razor blade, leave for 2 hours and again decapitate the apical 1 mm.

(*c*) Wrap a small piece of foil around the end of a match stick and place the foil over the end of a coleoptile so that the apical part is covered.

(*d*) Wrap a piece of foil around the body of a match stick so that a tube of foil is made about 18 mm long. Place this over the coleoptile so that only the top 2 mm is exposed.

(*e*) Decapitate a coleoptile as in (*b*) and apply a small amount of 500 mg dm^{-3} IAA in lanolin.

(*f*) Decapitate as in (*b*) and apply a small amount of plain lanolin paste.

Place the pots containing the seedlings in the box. After 1 day determine the curvature of the coleoptiles towards the light. Measure the degree of curvature from the vertical.

Discussion: The experiment described here is based on a familiar experiment to demonstrate phototropic response. Before starting the experiment, arbitrarily decide on a minimal curvature from the vertical which will be necessary to claim a response. It is suggested a 10° curvature would be suitable.

Table 14

Treatment	Angle of curvature
Intact	
Decapitated	
Tip covered	
Base covered	
Decapitated + IAA in lanolin	
Decapitated + lanolin	

77: To illustrate the light requirement of seeds for germination

Materials: Freshly harvested seeds of one of the species listed here: *Juncus* spp.; *Digitalis purpurea*; *Epilobium hirsutum*; dock; tobacco; birch
Petri dishes
Filter papers

Method: Sow freshly harvested seeds of one or more of the species mentioned above on moist filter paper in petri dishes, lining the lid of the dish with moist filter paper. Immediately after sowing, place half the dishes in the dark, and keep the other dishes in the light. Maintain both series of dishes at the same temperature. Record the germination in both series after 1 week.

The minimum period of light required for germination may be determined as follows:

Place *all dishes* in the dark immediately after sowing and on the following day expose two dishes each to 30 minutes, 1 hour, 2 hours and 4 hours light respectively, placing the dishes back in the dark after exposure. Keep all dishes in the dark for a further 5—6 days and then record the germination obtained with the different exposures.

Discussion: Many seeds require light for germination, e.g. *Juncus* spp., *Digitalis purpurea, Epilobium hirsutum, Lythrum salicaria*, tobacco, birch, dock, etc. The light-sensitivity varies with the age of the seed, the seed of many species being light-sensitive when freshly harvested but becoming less so with storage. The light responses are markedly affected by temperature: thus some seeds, e.g. some lettuce varieties, are light-requiring at $25°C$ but will germinate in the dark at cooler temperatures.

78: Imposing a light requirement for germination on seeds of lettuce

Materials: Lettuce seed var. Great Lakes
Petri dishes
Filter paper
80 mg dm^{-3} naringenin solution

Method: Line three petri dishes with doubled filter paper, moisten well with distilled water (one dish) or in a solution of 80 mg dm^{-3} naringenin (two dishes). Sow about 100 lettuce seeds of var. Great Lakes (not normally light requiring) in each dish and place in a cupboard *in complete darkness*.

After at least 2 hours for inhibition, bring out *one* of the naringenin-containing dishes into the daylight in the laboratory and leave for half an hour before replacing in the dark. It is most important that the two remaining 'dark' dishes are literally kept dark. Record the percentage germination.

Discussion: Naringenin is a germination and growth inhibitor which occurs in dormant peach buds, and it has been suggested that it may be concerned in the control of the state of dormancy of the buds. Some varieties of lettuce seeds will not germinate in the dark, whereas others will germinate in light or in dark but can be made light-requiring by the presence of an inhibitor.

9.2 Dormancy in plants

Almost all plants pass through a phase of dormancy at some stage in their life cycle. Usually this dormancy phase coincides with a time of year which is unfavourable for the growth of plants. If seeds shed in autumn were to germinate immediately they would reach the susceptible seedling stage at the time when winter frost began. Seeds therefore of many species, when shed, are innately dormant and are incapable of germinating despite favourable conditions. Following the dormant period, which will usually last the winter, the seed enters a period of post-dormancy or after-rest where dormancy gradually ceases and the percentage of seed germinating gradually rises. This dormancy may be due to a variety of causes. In certain families such as the *Leguminosae* the seed has an impermeable seed coat and cannot absorb oxygen or water even if they are readily available in the soil. Mechanical abrasion in the soil during the winter gradually breaks down the impermeable layers.

In a few species the embryo in the seed, when it is first shed, is immature and germination cannot take place until further embryo development has occurred. Seeds of *Anemone nemurosa* show a form of dormancy which is overcome by chilling. The site of action of the cold treatment may be in the seed coat as in *Betula pubescens* or in the embryo as in *Prunus persica*. In Hazel species both embryo and seed coat must be chilled.

In all experiments illustrating different types of seed dormancy freshly harvested seeds should be used.

Experiments 79–81

79: To demonstrate dormancy due to impermeable seed coats

Materials: Seeds of one of the following: clover, lupin, *Robinia pseudacacia*

Petri dishes
Filter paper
50% concentrated sulphuric acid

Method: Line two petri dishes with two layers of filter paper. Clip the seed coats of 20 seeds and place them in one dish on one side of a line drawn across the diameter of the dish in pencil. On the other side of the line, place 20 untreated seeds. Observe over several days. Place 20 seeds in 50% sulphuric acid for (*a*) 5 minutes, (*b*) 15 minutes, wash well in running water for 30 minutes and place in the remaining dish as above. Make observations on the germination after 1 week.

Discussion: Testa-imposed dormancy may be due to lack of penetration of water or impermeability to gases. In a few cases the testa may be so hard that it physically prevents radicle growth.

80: To illustrate embryo dormancy and testa-imposed dormancy

Materials: Seeds of ash, beech, mountain ash and sycamore
Petri dishes
Filter papers
100 cm^3 of 0.75% thiourea in water

Method (a):   With a scalpel *carefully* excise 10 embryos of ash, beech or mountain ash which have previously been soaked for several days. Take care not to let the embryos dry out, nor to damage them during excision. Place them on filter paper moistened with water in a petri dish. Line the lid of each petri dish with a second moist filter paper. To show that these embryos are capable of germination, excise a further 10 embryos and place on filter paper moistened with 0.75% thiourea solution. (Thiourea acts as a dormancy-breaking agent with the seeds of many species; many other chemicals, especially nitrates, will break dormancy.) Keep at room temperature and add additional water from time to time if required. Observe the germination of both samples of seed after 1 week.

Method (b):   With a pointed pair of forceps, *carefully* remove the pericarp and testa from 10 seeds of sycamore which have been soaked in water for 4 days. Particular care must be taken not to damage the radicle of the embryo which lies at the outer surface of the coiled cotyledons. Place the excised embryo on two moistened filter papers in a petri dish, and line the lid with a moist filter paper. Place 10 seeds with testas intact (but pericarps removed) on moist filter paper in a separate dish. Record the percentage germination for each dish after 1 and 2 weeks.

Discussion: Compounds inhibiting germination are frequently located in the seed coat. They will normally need to be leached out before germination can occur.

81: The removal of dormancy by chilling

Materials: Seeds of one of the following: apple, sycamore, beech, hazel or mountain ash
Seed trays or boxes
Sand or vermiculite
Refrigerator

Method: The effects of chilling in overcoming dormancy can be demonstrated for many of the above species of seed. This chilling effect may be demonstrated for both embryo dormancy and testa-imposed dormancy. In the autumn, plant a number of seeds of one of the named species in vermiculite or sand in pots or seed trays. Keep half the trays in a warm room, watering regularly. Leave the remaining trays out of doors during the winter. At the end of January, bring the latter pots indoors, watering as necessary. Compare the germination in the two series of treatments.

Alternatively, if a refrigerator is available, this may be used instead of placing plants out of doors. Keep the refrigerator at $0° - 5°C$. Plant the seeds in moist sand and keep in the refrigerator for at least 6 weeks, watering regularly as required.

Discussion: Chilling seeds may result in the destruction of a growth-inhibiting compound, but the exact mechanisms involved are likely to vary depending on the species.

9.3 Polarity in plants

Polarity may be defined as a characteristic orientation of organisms which is typically bipolar and axiate. It is a specific orientation of activity in space.

Polarity may manifest itself in many ways. The structures at the two ends of an axis are unlike, for example, roots and shoots, petiole and lamina in leaves. When regeneration occurs from small pieces of plant organs the organs formed at one end are different from those formed at the other. This is polarity expressing itself in morphogenesis. It may also express itself in transport systems within plants. The growth hormones, auxins, move from the tips of the plants back into the body of the plant and will not move in the reverse direction. This then is a polarity of movement.

The following experiments demonstrate both types of polarity.

Experiment 82

82: To illustrate polarity

Materials: Roots of dock or dandelion
Willow shoots
Razor blades
Flower pots
Peat
Bell-jar
Blotting paper

Method (a):   Cut dock or dandelion roots into 10 cm pieces with a square cut at the proximal end and a slanting cut at the distal end. Plant in pots of moist peat so that one-third are the 'correct' way up, one-third are on their side and one-third are inverted. Observe the growth of buds and roots and their relation to the tip and butt of the cuttings.

When the roots have appeared on half the cuttings trim them off. They will regrow. Repeat this several times. Observe any changes in development that may occur after several trimmings.

Method (b):   Take willow shoots and suspend half in the 'correct' and half in an inverted position in a bell-jar lined with wet blotting paper. Remove a ring of bark from the middle region of some of the shoots. Examine from time to time and record the growth of roots and buds.

Discussion: Repeated trimmings will result in loss to a variable extent of the polarity effect. This may be due to a loss of balance between hormones and nutritional status.

Projects

Experiment 76 describes a method of demonstrating the growth movement of plant organs in response to light. Gravity likewise can determine the direction of movement of these organs. To illustrate this germinate pea seeds for 36 hours and remove the seeds carefully. Lodge the seedling in the mouth of a test tube, holding it in position with damp cotton wool so that the root points vertically down. Arrange 15 such tubes vertically for 10 minutes. Take five of these tubes and place horizontally for 2–10 minutes. Determine the minimum time in the horizontal position which is necessary to induce a curvature (a curvature being arbitrarily decided as 10° movement away from the vertical). Other periods of stimulation may be used to increase accuracy.

The above suggested experiment assumes maximum stimulation is obtained by placing the root at 90° to the gravity stimulation. Test this by setting up a similar experiment allowing 6 minutes' stimulation time but placing the roots at 0–180° to the vertical. Determine the angle which gives maximum stimulation.

A further suggestion involves the concept that sub-threshold stimuli may be summated to bring about a response. Put a pea seedling in a tube as described and place horizontally. Stimulate for 2 minutes, return to the vertical for 2 minutes, restimulate for 2 minutes, return to the vertical and repeat. Six minutes should be enough to elicit a response. The above provides 6 minutes' stimulation, but interrupted. This should, however summate and induce a response.

Appendix 1　Buffers and pH

Consider a system where reactants A and B react together to form the products C and D:

$$A + B \rightleftharpoons C + D$$

The Law of Mass Action states that at equilibrium (where the rate of the forward reaction is equal to the rate of the back reaction) the product of the concentrations of C and D divided by the product of the concentrations of A and B is a constant. This is the equilibrium constant K.

$$K = \frac{[C]\,[D]}{[A]\,[B]}$$

where the brackets indicate concentrations of the species at equilibrium. The Law of Mass Action as applied to the dissociation of water shows:

$$K_w = \frac{[H^+]\,[OH^-]}{[H_2O]} \quad (K_w = \text{dissociation constant of water})$$

The equilibrium constant for this dissociation has been measured and shows that water dissociates only slightly to form H^+ and OH^- ions. The concentrations of these ions in pure water are both equal to $10^{-7}\,\text{mol dm}^{-3}$ ($10^{-7}\,\text{M}$). The product of these concentrations in any solution is found to be a constant:

$$[H^+]\,[OH^-] = 10^{-14}$$

Solutions will contain both ions and the relative proportions of the two determine the acidity or alkalinity of a solution. Thus in a neutral solution:

$$[H^+] = [OH^-] = 10^{-7}\,\text{mol dm}^{-3}$$

A convenient system of expressing the acidity or alkalinity of a solution is by the use of the logarithmic function, pH.

$$pH = \log \frac{1}{[H^+]} = -\log [H^+]$$

Consider a weak acid HA (a weak acid is one which has little tendency to dissociate), the Law of Mass Action shows:

$$K_a = \frac{[H^+][A^-]}{[HA]} \quad (K_a = \text{dissociation constant of weak acid})$$

Rearranging the terms

$$[H^+] = \frac{K[HA]}{[A^-]}$$

Taking logs of the terms

$$\log [H^+] = \log K + \log \frac{[HA]}{[A^-]}$$

Multiplying by (−1)

$$-\log [H^+] = -\log K - \log \frac{[HA]}{[A^-]}$$

By definition $-\log [H^+]$ is pH and $-\log K$ is defined as pK, if $\log [A^-]/[HA]$ is substituted for $-\log [HA]/[A^-]$ then:

$$pH = pK + \log \frac{[A^-]}{[HA]}$$

This is the Henderson−Hasselbach equation which is of great value in calculating the pH of mixtures of weak acids and their salts—buffer solutions. A buffer solution is one which stabilises the H^+ concentration, that is it resists changes in pH on the addition of acid and/or alkali.

An example of a buffer solution is given by a mixture of ethanoic acid (acetic acid) and sodium ethanoate (sodium acetate). Applying the Henderson−Hasselbach equation to the behaviour of ethanoic acid:

$$CH_3COOH \rightleftharpoons CH_3COO^- + H^+$$

$$pH = pK + \log \frac{[CH_3COO^-]}{[CH_3COOH]}$$

As K, and therefore pK, is a constant, the equation indicates that the pH of this solution is determined by the ratio of ethanoate to ethanoic acid or in general terms to the salt/acid ratio.

An understanding of the mechanism whereby a buffer stabilises the pH of a solution may be gained from the following example. In an ethanoate buffer the components will behave as follows:

$$CH_3COONa \longrightarrow CH_3COO^- + Na^+$$

$$CH_3COOH \rightleftharpoons CH_3COO^- + H^+$$

The salt will be completely dissociated whilst the acid will be only partially dissociated. If extra H^+ ions are added to the system they will react with the ethanoate ions to form undissociated ethanoic acid. If additional OH^- ions are added they will combine with H^+ ions to form water. The H^+ ions removed from the system are replaced by further dissociation of the ethanoic acid.

The cytoplasm of all organisms is able to act as a buffer system and maintain the internal environment of cells at a constant pH. The cellular enzymes responsible for catalysing metabolic reactions exhibit their action within a definite pH range (see Chapter 4). Thus the ability to prevent large changes in pH is of fundamental importance to biological systems. In many experiments pH is stabilised by the use of buffers made up of mixtures of weak acids and their salts, e.g. ethanoic acid/ethanoate, citric acid/citrate and phosphoric acid/phosphate.

Table 15 Buffer table: relative volumes (cm^3) required to give particular pH

pH	cm^3 of 1/15 mol dm^{-3} K$_2$HPO$_4$ (M/15 K$_2$HPO$_4$)	cm^3 of 1/15 mol dm^{-3} K$_2$HPO$_4$ (M/15 KH$_2$PO$_4$)
5.0	0.2	9.8
5.5	0.6	9.4
6.0	1.7	8.3
6.5	3.8	6.2
7.0	6.7	3.3
7.5	8.6	1.4
8.0	9.5	0.5

Appendix 2   Chromatography

Chromatography is a technique for separating a mixture of substances. Separation is achieved by the distribution of substances between two phases — the stationary and the mobile phase. Separation occurs when one substance is held more strongly by the stationary phase and may be more soluble in the solvent than the other substance(s) which tend to move on faster in the mobile phase. All techniques of chromatography are based upon this principle.

Adsorption chromatography uses a solid as the stationary phase with a liquid as the mobile phase. Separation of a mixture occurs when one component is more strongly adsorbed by the solid than the other component(s) and possibly more soluble in the solvent.

Partition chromatography uses a liquid as the stationary phase. The liquid is usually water held on an inert porous solid such as cellulose. The mobile phase is a liquid mixture (or a gas). Separation occurs when one component is more strongly retained than the other(s) by the stationary phase.

Paper chromatography

Paper chromatography is an example of partition chromatography. The separation of a mixture of substances is achieved by their partition between the water in the cellulose fibres of the paper and the solvent flowing over the paper. The mixture is applied at the origin and the paper is placed with one end in the solvent so that the origin is free of the solvent. The solvent rises up the paper by capillarity.

Any air-tight container can serve as the tank for the solvent although a glass vessel is preferable as it is easier to clean. The tank must be large enough to accommodate the height of the paper. Prepare the solvent and place in the tank to a depth of 1 cm. Replace the tank lid and allow the solvent to equilibrate for 15 minutes to saturate the atmosphere before the paper is placed in the solvent. The temperature of the room used for chromatography should be kept as constant as possible. The application of the spot to the paper may be made using a microsyringe, capillary tube or a small (4 mm diameter) platinum loop. The platinum loop has the advantage that samples may be applied and the residue washed and then burnt off in a flame before application of the next sample; syringes and capillary tubes need to be scrupulously cleaned between sample applications.

Preparation

Take or cut a sheet of Whatman No. 1 paper. Draw a pencil line 2.5 cm from the edge of the paper. Along this line space dots every 2.5 cm. These dots will serve as the origins for the spots to be applied. Label each dot in pencil below the line for identification. Spot a small drop of each substance on to the dots (one substance per dot), keeping the diameter of each spot as small as possible and preferably less than 1 cm. (If a greater concentration is required on each dot than is given by one spot, the first spot must be allowed to dry and a second spot of the same substance then added. A hair-drier can be used to speed drying.)

When the spots are dry, roll the paper in a cylinder form and fasten the edges with two staples or small paper clips or cotton. Place the chromatogram (spotted end down) into the solvent, ensuring the solvent level is below the origin and that the paper does not touch the sides or lid of the tank. Replace the lid. When the chromatogram has run for the desired time (allow the solvent to run about 75% of the length of paper) remove it from the tank and mark in pencil the position of the solvent front. Dry the paper rapidly with a hair-drier in a fume cupboard. The spots may be located either by dipping the paper in a tray filled with locating reagent or by spraying using an aerosol or atomiser containing locating reagent.

Thin Layer Chromatography (TLC)

TLC is an example of adsorption chromatography. The method relies upon coating a glass plate with a thin layer of adsorbent material. Microscope or lantern slides are suitable as plates but must be free from grease (if necessary clean with acetone). Silica gel may be used as an adsorbent prepared for use by adding 2 ml of deionised water for every 1 g of silica gel and quickly mixing until the slurry is homogenous. (Approximately 10 cm^2 of plate requires 2.5 g of silica gel.) The prepared slurry sets within 2—3 minutes and the coated plates must be activated by drying at 90°—100°C for 30 minutes. If the slurry is prepared with chloroform it will not set and will keep indefinitely in an air-tight container. Plates prepared with this type of slurry are ready as soon as the chloroform has evaporated, although activity is enhanced by drying in the oven for 3—4 minutes.

Many coating devices are available commercially and most involve a moving spreader and stationary glass plates. There are however several methods for producing thin layers on plates without special equipment. These include:

1. Microscope slides may be coated simply by placing two slides back to back and dipping into a beaker of the adsorbent slurry.
2. One to three layers of surgical or masking tapes are put on opposite edges of a plate on a flat surface. The adsorbent slurry is poured on one end of the plate and smoothed by drawing a glass rod over the taped plate. After a few minutes the tape is removed and the plates dried.
3. Ridged glass plates offer a very simple method. The adsorbent slurry is poured on the plate and scraped off with a spatula before and after drying, to leave layers between the ridges. Coated plates may be stored in a desiccator over calcium chloride.

Preparation

The coated plate cannot be marked in the same way as paper can, and so two marks are made on either side of the plate level with the origin. The samples are applied in the same way as for paper chromatography. Any air-tight vessel will serve for a tank. Add sufficient solvent to the tank and equilibrate as before. Lower the spotted plate (origin down) into the solvent making sure the solvent is below the origin and replace the lid. When the plate is removed from the tank, blot the lower edge, mark the position of the solvent front with a needle and then dry the plate in an oven. Spots are located by spraying the plate with the appropriate locating reagent.

Results

The migration of a substance relative to the solvent front is characteristic of the substance. This is the R_f value (see Fig. 18).

$$R_f = \frac{\text{Distance moved by the substance}}{\text{Distance moved by the solvent front}} = \frac{x}{y}$$

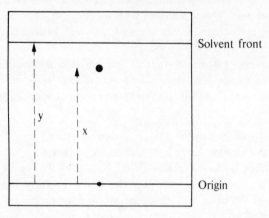

Fig. 18   A chromatogram

Identification of the spots may be achieved by comparing their R_f values with those of known compounds ('markers') run on the same chromatograms.

Appendix 3   Colorimetry

Most materials will absorb light energy of particular wavelengths. Proteins, for example, strongly absorb u.v. light. Many compounds of biological interest are coloured or will form coloured compounds on treatment with suitable reagents and so may be estimated by colorimetry.

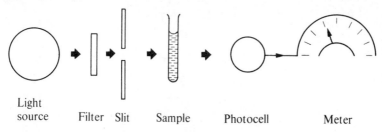

Light
source   Filter Slit   Sample   Photocell   Meter

Fig. 19   Diagrammatic representation of a colorimeter

A diagrammatic representation of a colorimeter is shown in Fig. 19. The instrument has a polychromatic light source. Light from the source passes through a slit to the solution under investigation. Any light transmitted through the solution, i.e. light not absorbed by the solution, is then measured using a photo-electric cell. To increase the accuracy of the instrument it is usual to place a coloured filter between the light source and the solution so that it is the absorption of light within a limited range of wavelengths which is measured. The correct filter for any determination is of the colour complementary to that of the solution, i.e. the colour or wavelength at which maximum light absorption occurs in the sample.

The measurement of concentration of a given substance requires a blank and a series of standards. The blank solution provides a reference against which the colorimeter may be set to zero (no absorption of light). To offset the effect of any colour in the reagents used, the blank should consist of the mixture of reagents used in preparing the sample, and distilled water should replace the sample. The difference in colour between the blank and the sample is then due only to the sample. It is essential that the same volume of reagents be used for every sample and blank and that the final volume of each treated sample and blank be the same. The standard solutions contain a range of known concentrations of the given substance.

Appendix 4   Determination of standard error and deviation

Statistical analysis of numerical data obtained by measuring growth in terms of root length, fresh mass, dry mass, etc., is essential. One of the simplest methods of analysis is the determination of variability by the determination of 'standard deviations'.

This determination becomes necessary because in a sample of, say, 20 plants the individuals may vary so much as to render the mean value quite useless. If the two sets of figures below are compared, it can be seen that they both have the same average or mean but that in the second case this is a meaningless figure.

Series 1   10, 12, 10, 14, 12, 14   Mean = 12
Series 2   6, 4, 18, 13, 4, 23   Mean = 12

The standard deviation is a measure of the meaningfulness of the mean of a particular set of figures.

The mean of a given set of figures is written $(\bar{x})$; the individual observations (X_i); the total number of individuals (N).

To determine the standard deviation first determine $(\bar{x})$ by adding all the individual observations and dividing by the total number of individuals.

This can best be illustrated by an example of 20 fresh-mass-determinations (Table 16).

In an experiment it is usual to compare treated with untreated plants or treated with control plants. With the results of the experiment described we can calculate a mean for treated and untreated plants and a standard deviation. This gives us an opportunity to compare the two treatments. If the difference between the two means is larger than twice the standard error of the difference, it can be concluded that the difference is not due to random change alone, i.e. the difference between treated and untreated plants is significant.

To calculate the standard error of the difference of two different means apply the following equation.

Table 16

Observation (Fresh mass in mg) (X_i)	Deviation from mean $(X_i - \bar{x})$	*$(X_i - \bar{x})^2$
39.0	−1.0	1.0
41.2	+1.2	1.44
36.4	−3.6	12.96
38.3	−1.7	2.89
41.0	+1.0	1.0
40.8	+0.8	0.64
37.9	−2.1	4.41
42.1	+2.1	4.41
40.7	+0.7	0.49
41.3	+1.3	1.69
42.1	+2.1	4.41
38.3	−1.7	2.89
41.5	+1.5	2.33
37.7	−2.3	5.29
38.1	−1.9	3.61
42.3	+2.3	5.29
41.6	+1.6	2.56
41.0	+1.0	1.0
39.0	−1.0	1.0
39.8	−0.2	0.04
800.1	0	59.35 = $\Sigma(X_i - \bar{x})^2$

$$\text{Mean } (\bar{X}) = \frac{\text{Total } (\Sigma(X_i))}{\text{No. of determinations } (N)} = \frac{800.1}{20} = 40.0 \text{ mg}$$

$$\text{Standard Deviation of Sample} = \sqrt{\frac{\Sigma(X_i - \bar{x})^2}{N - 1}}$$

$$= \sqrt{\frac{59.35}{19}} = \sqrt{3.123} = 1.767$$

* The deviation from the mean is squared so that you can deal with positive values.

The mean ± one standard deviation will cover about 66% of all the observed cases in randomly distributed populations.

In the above case 40.0 mg ± 1.767.

$$\text{S.E. } \bar{x}_1 - \bar{x}_2 = \sqrt{\frac{S_1^2}{\sqrt{N_1}} + \frac{S_2^2}{\sqrt{N_2}}}$$

Where S_1 and S_2 = standard deviations of two samples

N_1 and N_2 = number of individuals in the two samples

$\bar{x}_1$ and $\bar{x}_2$ = means of the samples.

Appendix 5   SI units

Volume

The SI unit of volume is the cubic metre, m^3. In many institutions laboratory glassware will still be calibrated in litres, ml, or μl. The following volumes are related to fractions of a cubic metre:

$1 \text{ litre} = 1 \text{ dm}^3 = 10^{-3} \text{ m}^3$

$1 \text{ millilitre} = 1 \text{ cm}^3 = 10^{-6} \text{ m}^3$

$1 \text{ microlitre} = 1 \text{ mm}^3 = 10^{-9} \text{ m}^3$

Weight

The SI unit of mass is the kilogram, kg.

$1 \text{ gramme} = 10^{-3} \text{ kg}$

$1 \text{ milligramme} = 10^{-6} \text{ kg}$ (this may still quite properly be expressed as milligrams, mg)

$1 \text{ microgramme} = 10^{-9} \text{ kg}$ ($1 \mu g$)

Concentration

Molarity, M, indicates the amount of solute in moles, dissolved in 1 litre of solution.

In SI units a 1 M solution has a concentration of
$10^3 \text{ mol m}^{-3} = 1 \text{ kmol m}^{-3} = 1 \text{ mol dm}^{-3}$.

For ease of conversion of molarities into their SI equivalents, it is easier to use the mol dm^{-3} nomenclature.

Temperature

The SI unit of temperature is the kelvin, K.

1 K = 1/273.16 of the thermodynamic temperature of the triple point of water.

$0°C = 273.15$ K.

Pressure

The SI unit of pressure is the Pascal, Pa.

Pressures should therefore be expressed in Pa or in Nm^{-2}
(1 atmosphere (atm) = 101 325 Pa = 101 325 Nm^{-2}).

Appendix 6 Major plant growth hormones

Identity	Molecular mass	Structure
β-Indolyl acetic acid (IAA)	175	
Gibberellic acid (GA$_3$)	346	
Kinetin	215	
Abscisic acid	264	

Index